TEACHER'S GUIDE

W9-ATI-563

Connected Mathematics 2™

Comparing and Scaling

Ratio, Proportion, and Percent

BOWLING GREEN STATE UNIVERSITY
DISCARDED
LIBRARY

Glenda Lappan
James T. Fey
William M. Fitzgerald
Susan N. Friel
Elizabeth Difanis Phillips

PEARSON

BOWLING GREEN STATE
UNIVERSITY LIBRARIES

Boston, Massachusetts · Glenview, Illinois · Shoreview, Minnesota · Upper Saddle River, New Jersey

Connected Mathematics™ was developed at Michigan State University with financial support from the Michigan State University Office of the Provost, Computing and Technology, and the College of Natural Science.

This material is based upon work supported by the National Science Foundation under Grant No. MDR 9150217 and Grant No. ESI 9986372. Opinions expressed are those of the authors and not necessarily those of the Foundation.

The Michigan State University authors and administration have agreed that all MSU royalties arising from this publication will be devoted to purposes supported by the Department of Mathematics and the MSU Mathematics Enrichment Fund.

Acknowledgments appear on page 113, which constitutes an extension of this copyright page. **Acknowledgments** for the student pages appear on student page 74, which constitutes an extension of this copyright page.

Copyright © 2009 by Michigan State University, Glenda Lappan, James T. Fey, William M. Fitzgerald, Susan N. Friel, and Elizabeth D. Phillips. Published by Pearson Education, Inc. All rights reserved. Printed in the United States of America. This publication is protected by copyright, and permission should be obtained from the publisher prior to any prohibited reproduction, storage in a retrieval system, or transmission in any form or by any means, electronic, mechanical, photocopying, recording, or likewise. Student worksheets may be duplicated for classroom use, the number not to exceed the number of students in each class. Notice of copyright must appear on all copies. For information regarding permissions, write to Rights and Permissions Department, Pearson School, One Lake Street, Upper Saddle River, New Jersey 07458.

Prentice Hall® and **Pearson Prentice Hall™** are trademarks, in the U.S. and/or in other countries, of Pearson Education, Inc., or its affiliate(s).

ExamView® is a registered trademark of FSCreations, Inc.

Connected Mathematics™ is a trademark of Michigan State University.

13-digit ISBN 978-0-13-366194-1
10-digit ISBN 0-13-366194-6
1 2 3 4 5 6 7 8 9 10   11 10 09 08

Authors of Connected Mathematics

(from left to right) Glenda Lappan, Betty Phillips, Susan Friel, Bill Fitzgerald, Jim Fey

Glenda Lappan is a University Distinguished Professor in the Department of Mathematics at Michigan State University. Her research and development interests are in the connected areas of students' learning of mathematics and mathematics teachers' professional growth and change related to the development and enactment of K–12 curriculum materials.

James T. Fey is a Professor of Curriculum and Instruction and Mathematics at the University of Maryland. His consistent professional interest has been development and research focused on curriculum materials that engage middle and high school students in problem-based collaborative investigations of mathematical ideas and their applications.

William M. Fitzgerald (*Deceased*) was a Professor in the Department of Mathematics at Michigan State University. His early research was on the use of concrete materials in supporting student learning and led to the development of teaching materials for laboratory environments. Later he helped develop a teaching model to support student experimentation with mathematics.

Susan N. Friel is a Professor of Mathematics Education in the School of Education at the University of North Carolina at Chapel Hill. Her research interests focus on statistics education for middle-grade students and, more broadly, on teachers' professional development and growth in teaching mathematics K–8.

Elizabeth Difanis Phillips is a Senior Academic Specialist in the Mathematics Department of Michigan State University. She is interested in teaching and learning mathematics for both teachers and students. These interests have led to curriculum and professional development projects at the middle school and high school levels, as well as projects related to the teaching and learning of algebra across the grades.

CMP2 Development Staff

Teacher Collaborator in Residence
Yvonne Grant
Michigan State University

Administrative Assistant
Judith Martus Miller
Michigan State University

Production and Field Site Manager
Lisa Keller
Michigan State University

Technical and Editorial Support
Brin Keller, Peter Lappan, Jim Laser,
Michael Masterson, Stacey Miceli

Assessment Team

June Bailey and Debra Sobko (Apollo Middle School, Rochester, New York), George Bright (University of North Carolina, Greensboro), Gwen Ranzau Campbell (Sunrise Park Middle School, White Bear Lake, Minnesota), Holly DeRosia, Kathy Dole, and Teri Keusch (Portland Middle School, Portland, Michigan), Mary Beth Schmitt (Traverse City East Junior High School, Traverse City, Michigan), Genni Steele (Central Middle School, White Bear Lake, Minnesota), Jacqueline Stewart (Okemos, Michigan), Elizabeth Tye (Magnolia Junior High School, Magnolia, Arkansas)

Development Assistants

At Lansing Community College *Undergraduate Assistant:* James Brinegar

At Michigan State University *Graduate Assistants:* Dawn Berk, Emily Bouck, Bulent Buyukbozkirli, Kuo-Liang Chang, Christopher Danielson, Srinivasa Dharmavaram, Deb Johanning, Wesley Kretzschmar, Kelly Rivette, Sarah Sword, Tat Ming Sze, Marie Turini, Jeffrey Wanko; *Undergraduate Assistants:* Daniel Briggs, Jeffrey Chapin, Jade Corsé, Elisha Hardy, Alisha Harold, Elizabeth Keusch, Julia Letoutchaia, Karen Loeffler, Brian Oliver, Carl Oliver, Evonne Pedawi, Lauren Rebrovich

At the University of Maryland *Graduate Assistants:* Kim Harris Bethea, Kara Karch

At the University of North Carolina (Chapel Hill) *Graduate Assistants:* Mark Ellis, Trista Stearns; *Undergraduate Assistant:* Daniel Smith

Advisory Board for CMP2

Thomas Banchoff
Professor of Mathematics
Brown University
Providence, Rhode Island

Anne Bartel
Mathematics Coordinator
Minneapolis Public Schools
Minneapolis, Minnesota

Hyman Bass
Professor of Mathematics
University of Michigan
Ann Arbor, Michigan

Joan Ferrini-Mundy
Associate Dean of the College of
Natural Science; Professor
Michigan State University
East Lansing, Michigan

James Hiebert
Professor
University of Delaware
Newark, Delaware

Susan Hudson Hull
Charles A. Dana Center
University of Texas
Austin, Texas

Michele Luke
Mathematics Curriculum
Coordinator
West Junior High
Minnetonka, Minnesota

Kay McClain
Assistant Professor of
Mathematics Education
Vanderbilt University
Nashville, Tennessee

Edward Silver
Professor; Chair of Educational
Studies
University of Michigan
Ann Arbor, Michigan

Judith Sowder
Professor Emerita
San Diego State University
San Diego, California

Lisa Usher
Mathematics Resource Teacher
California Academy of
Mathematics and Science
San Pedro, California

Field Test Sites for CMP2

During the development of the revised edition of *Connected Mathematics* (CMP2), more than 100 classroom teachers have field-tested materials at 49 school sites in 12 states and the District of Columbia. This classroom testing occurred over three academic years (2001 through 2004), allowing careful study of the effectiveness of each of the 24 units that comprise the program. A special thanks to the students and teachers at these pilot schools.

Arkansas
Magnolia Public Schools
Kittena Bell*, Judith Trowell*; *Central Elementary School:* Maxine Broom, Betty Eddy, Tiffany Fallin, Bonnie Flurry, Carolyn Monk, Elizabeth Tye; *Magnolia Junior High School:* Monique Bryan, Ginger Cook, David Graham, Shelby Lamkin

Colorado
Boulder Public Schools
Nevin Platt Middle School: Judith Koenig

St. Vrain Valley School District, Longmont
Westview Middle School: Colleen Beyer, Kitty Canupp, Ellie Decker*, Peggy McCarthy, Tanya deNobrega, Cindy Payne, Ericka Pilon, Andrew Roberts

District of Columbia
Capitol Hill Day School: Ann Lawrence

Georgia
University of Georgia, Athens
Brad Findell

Madison Public Schools
Morgan County Middle School: Renee Burgdorf, Lynn Harris, Nancy Kurtz, Carolyn Stewart

Maine
Falmouth Public Schools
Falmouth Middle School: Donna Erikson, Joyce Hebert, Paula Hodgkins, Rick Hogan, David Legere, Cynthia Martin, Barbara Stiles, Shawn Towle*

---

* indicates a Field Test Site Coordinator

Michigan
Portland Public Schools
Portland Middle School: Mark Braun, Holly DeRosia, Kathy Dole*, Angie Foote, Teri Keusch, Tammi Wardwell

Traverse City Area Public Schools
Bertha Vos Elementary: Kristin Sak; *Central Grade School:* Michelle Clark; Jody Meyers; *Eastern Elementary:* Karrie Tufts; *Interlochen Elementary:* Mary McGee-Cullen; *Long Lake Elementary:* Julie Faulkner*, Charlie Maxbauer, Katherine Sleder; *Norris Elementary:* Hope Slanaker; *Oak Park Elementary:* Jessica Steed; *Traverse Heights Elementary:* Jennifer Wolfert; *Westwoods Elementary:* Nancy Conn; *Old Mission Peninsula School:* Deb Larimer; *Traverse City East Junior High:* Ivanka Berkshire, Ruthanne Kladder, Jan Palkowski, Jane Peterson, Mary Beth Schmitt; *Traverse City West Junior High:* Dan Fouch*, Ray Fouch

Sturgis Public Schools
Sturgis Middle School: Ellen Eisele

Minnesota
Burnsville School District 191
Hidden Valley Elementary: Stephanie Cin, Jane McDevitt

Hopkins School District 270
Alice Smith Elementary: Sandra Cowing, Kathleen Gustafson, Martha Mason, Scott Stillman; *Eisenhower Elementary:* Chad Bellig, Patrick Berger, Nancy Glades, Kye Johnson, Shane Wasserman, Victoria Wilson; *Gatewood Elementary:* Sarah Ham, Julie Kloos, Janine Pung, Larry Wade; *Glen Lake Elementary:* Jacqueline Cramer, Kathy Hering, Cecelia Morris, Robb Trenda; *Katherine Curren Elementary:* Diane Bancroft, Sue DeWit, John Wilson; *L. H. Tanglen Elementary:* Kevin Athmann, Lisa Becker, Mary LaBelle, Kathy Rezac, Roberta Severson; *Meadowbrook Elementary:* Jan Gauger, Hildy Shank, Jessica Zimmerman; *North Junior High:* Laurel Hahn, Kristin Lee, Jodi Markuson, Bruce Mestemacher, Laurel Miller, Bonnie Rinker, Jeannine Salzer, Sarah Shafer, Cam Stottler; *West Junior High:* Alicia Beebe, Kristie Earl, Nobu Fujii, Pam Georgetti, Susan Gilbert, Regina Nelson Johnson, Debra Lindstrom, Michele Luke*, Jon Sorensen

Minneapolis School District 1
Ann Sullivan K–8 School: Bronwyn Collins; Anne Bartel* (Curriculum and Instruction Office)

Wayzata School District 284
Central Middle School: Sarajane Myers, Dan Nielsen, Tanya Ravnholdt

White Bear Lake School District 624
Central Middle School: Amy Jorgenson, Michelle Reich, Brenda Sammon

New York
New York City Public Schools
IS 89: Yelena Aynbinder, Chi-Man Ng, Nina Rapaport, Joel Spengler, Phyllis Tam*, Brent Wyso; *Wagner Middle School:* Jason Appel, Intissar Fernandez, Yee Gee Get, Richard Goldstein, Irving Marcus, Sue Norton, Bernadita Owens, Jennifer Rehn*, Kevin Yuhas

Ohio

Talawanda School District, Oxford
Talawanda Middle School: Teresa Abrams, Larry Brock, Heather Brosey, Julie Churchman, Monna Even, Karen Fitch, Bob George, Amanda Klee, Pat Meade, Sandy Montgomery, Barbara Sherman, Lauren Steidl

Miami University
Jeffrey Wanko*

Springfield Public Schools
Rockway School: Jim Mamer

Pennsylvania

Pittsburgh Public Schools
Kenneth Labuskes, Marianne O'Connor, Mary Lynn Raith*; *Arthur J. Rooney Middle School:* David Hairston, Stamatina Mousetis, Alfredo Zangaro; *Frick International Studies Academy:* Suzanne Berry, Janet Falkowski, Constance Finseth, Romika Hodge, Frank Machi; *Reizenstein Middle School:* Jeff Baldwin, James Brautigam, Lorena Burnett, Glen Cobbett, Michael Jordan, Margaret Lazur, Tamar McPherson, Melissa Munnell, Holly Neely, Ingrid Reed, Dennis Reft

Texas

Austin Independent School District
Bedichek Middle School: Lisa Brown, Jennifer Glasscock, Vicki Massey

El Paso Independent School District
Cordova Middle School: Armando Aguirre, Anneliesa Durkes, Sylvia Guzman, Pat Holguin*, William Holguin, Nancy Nava, Laura Orozco, Michelle Peña, Roberta Rosen, Patsy Smith, Jeremy Wolf

Plano Independent School District
Patt Henry, James Wohlgehagen*; *Frankford Middle School:* Mandy Baker, Cheryl Butsch, Amy Dudley, Betsy Eshelman, Janet Greene, Cort Haynes, Kathy Letchworth, Kay Marshall, Kelly McCants, Amy Reck, Judy Scott, Syndy Snyder, Lisa Wang; *Wilson Middle School:* Darcie Bane, Amanda Bedenko, Whitney Evans, Tonelli Hatley, Sarah (Becky) Higgs, Kelly Johnston, Rebecca McElligott, Kay Neuse, Cheri Slocum, Kelli Straight

Washington

Evergreen School District
Shahala Middle School: Nicole Abrahamsen, Terry Coon*, Carey Doyle, Sheryl Drechsler, George Gemma, Gina Helland, Amy Hilario, Darla Lidyard, Sean McCarthy, Tilly Meyer, Willow Nuewelt, Todd Parsons, Brian Pederson, Stan Posey, Shawn Scott, Craig Sjoberg, Lynette Sundstrom, Charles Switzer, Luke Youngblood

Wisconsin

Beaver Dam Unified School District
Beaver Dam Middle School: Jim Braemer, Jeanne Frick, Jessica Greatens, Barbara Link, Dennis McCormick, Karen Michels, Nancy Nichols*, Nancy Palm, Shelly Stelsel, Susan Wiggins

---

* indicates a Field Test Site Coordinator

Reviews of CMP to Guide Development of CMP2

Before writing for CMP2 began or field tests were conducted, the first edition of *Connected Mathematics* was submitted to the mathematics faculties of school districts from many parts of the country and to 80 individual reviewers for extensive comments.

School District Survey Reviews of CMP

Arizona
Madison School District #38 (Phoenix)

Arkansas
Cabot School District, Little Rock School District, Magnolia School District

California
Los Angeles Unified School District

Colorado
St. Vrain Valley School District (Longmont)

Florida
Leon County Schools (Tallahassee)

Illinois
School District #21 (Wheeling)

Indiana
Joseph L. Block Junior High (East Chicago)

Kentucky
Fayette County Public Schools (Lexington)

Maine
Selection of Schools

Massachusetts
Selection of Schools

Michigan
Sparta Area Schools

Minnesota
Hopkins School District

Texas
Austin Independent School District, The El Paso Collaborative for Academic Excellence, Plano Independent School District

Wisconsin
Platteville Middle School

Individual Reviewers of CMP

Arkansas
Deborah Cramer; Robby Frizzell *(Taylor)*; Lowell Lynde *(University of Arkansas, Monticello)*; Leigh Manzer *(Norfork)*; Lynne Roberts *(Emerson High School, Emerson)*; Tony Timms *(Cabot Public Schools)*; Judith Trowell *(Arkansas Department of Higher Education)*

California
José Alcantar *(Gilroy)*; Eugenie Belcher *(Gilroy)*; Marian Pasternack *(Lowman M. S. T. Center, North Hollywood)*; Susana Pezoa *(San Jose)*; Todd Rabusin *(Hollister)*; Margaret Siegfried *(Ocala Middle School, San Jose)*; Polly Underwood *(Ocala Middle School, San Jose)*

Colorado
Janeane Golliher *(St. Vrain Valley School District, Longmont)*; Judith Koenig *(Nevin Platt Middle School, Boulder)*

Florida
Paige Loggins *(Swift Creek Middle School, Tallahassee)*

Illinois
Jan Robinson *(School District #21, Wheeling)*

Indiana
Frances Jackson *(Joseph L. Block Junior High, East Chicago)*

Kentucky
Natalee Feese *(Fayette County Public Schools, Lexington)*

Maine
Betsy Berry *(Maine Math & Science Alliance, Augusta)*

Maryland
Joseph Gagnon *(University of Maryland, College Park)*; Paula Maccini *(University of Maryland, College Park)*

Massachusetts
George Cobb *(Mt. Holyoke College, South Hadley)*; Cliff Kanold *(University of Massachusetts, Amherst)*

Michigan
Mary Bouck *(Farwell Area Schools)*; Carol Dorer *(Slauson Middle School, Ann Arbor)*; Carrie Heaney *(Forsythe Middle School, Ann Arbor)*; Ellen Hopkins *(Clague Middle School, Ann Arbor)*; Teri Keusch *(Portland Middle School, Portland)*; Valerie Mills *(Oakland Schools, Waterford)*; Mary Beth Schmitt *(Traverse City East Junior High, Traverse City)*; Jack Smith *(Michigan State University, East Lansing)*; Rebecca Spencer *(Sparta Middle School, Sparta)*; Ann Marie Nicoll Turner *(Tappan Middle School, Ann Arbor)*; Scott Turner *(Scarlett Middle School, Ann Arbor)*

Minnesota
Margarita Alvarez *(Olson Middle School, Minneapolis)*; Jane Amundson *(Nicollet Junior High, Burnsville)*; Anne Bartel *(Minneapolis Public Schools)*; Gwen Ranzau Campbell *(Sunrise Park Middle School, White Bear Lake)*; Stephanie Cin *(Hidden Valley Elementary, Burnsville)*; Joan Garfield *(University of Minnesota, Minneapolis)*; Gretchen Hall *(Richfield Middle School, Richfield)*; Jennifer Larson *(Olson Middle School, Minneapolis)*; Michele Luke *(West Junior High, Minnetonka)*; Jeni Meyer *(Richfield Junior High, Richfield)*; Judy Pfingsten *(Inver Grove Heights Middle School, Inver Grove Heights)*; Sarah Shafer *(North Junior High, Minnetonka)*; Genni Steele *(Central Middle School, White Bear Lake)*; Victoria Wilson *(Eisenhower Elementary, Hopkins)*; Paul Zorn *(St. Olaf College, Northfield)*

New York
Debra Altenau-Bartolino *(Greenwich Village Middle School, New York)*; Doug Clements *(University of Buffalo)*; Francis Curcio *(New York University, New York)*; Christine Dorosh *(Clinton School for Writers, Brooklyn)*; Jennifer Rehn *(East Side Middle School, New York)*; Phyllis Tam *(IS 89 Lab School, New York)*;

Marie Turini *(Louis Armstrong Middle School, New York)*; Lucy West *(Community School District 2, New York)*; Monica Witt *(Simon Baruch Intermediate School 104, New York)*

Pennsylvania
Robert Aglietti *(Pittsburgh)*; Sharon Mihalich *(Freeport)*; Jennifer Plumb *(South Hills Middle School, Pittsburgh)*; Mary Lynn Raith *(Pittsburgh Public Schools)*

Texas
Michelle Bittick *(Austin Independent School District)*; Margaret Cregg *(Plano Independent School District)*; Sheila Cunningham *(Klein Independent School District)*; Judy Hill *(Austin Independent School District)*; Patricia Holguin *(El Paso Independent School District)*; Bonnie McNemar *(Arlington)*; Kay Neuse *(Plano Independent School District)*; Joyce Polanco *(Austin Independent School District)*; Marge Ramirez *(University of Texas at El Paso)*; Pat Rossman *(Baker Campus, Austin)*; Cindy Schimek *(Houston)*; Cynthia Schneider *(Charles A. Dana Center, University of Texas at Austin)*; Uri Treisman *(Charles A. Dana Center, University of Texas at Austin)*; Jacqueline Weilmuenster *(Grapevine-Colleyville Independent School District)*; LuAnn Weynand *(San Antonio)*; Carmen Whitman *(Austin Independent School District)*; James Wohlgehagen *(Plano Independent School District)*

Washington
Ramesh Gangolli *(University of Washington, Seattle)*

Wisconsin
Susan Lamon *(Marquette University, Hales Corner)*; Steve Reinhart *(retired, Chippewa Falls Middle School, Eau Claire)*

Comparing and Scaling
Ratio, Proportion, and Percent

> The Student Edition pages for the Unit Opener follow page 12.

Unit Introduction

Comparing and Scaling
Ratio, Proportion, and Percent

Goals of the Unit

- Analyze comparison statements made about quantitative data

- Use ratios, fractions, differences, and percents to form comparison statements in a given situation, such as

  "What is the ratio of boys to girls in our class?"

  "What fraction of the class is going to the spring picnic?"

  "What percent of the girls play basketball?"

  "Which model of car has the best fuel economy?"

- Judge whether comparison statements make sense and are useful

- See how forms of comparison statements are related (for example, a percent and a fraction comparison)

- Make judgments about which statements are most informative or best reflect a particular point of view

- Decide when the most informative comparison is the difference between two quantities and when it is a ratio between pairs of quantities

- Scale a ratio, rate, or fraction to make a larger or smaller object or population with the same relative characteristics as the original

- Represent related data in tables

- Look for patterns in tables that will allow predictions to be made beyond the tables

- Write an equation to represent the pattern in a table of related variables

- Apply proportional reasoning to solve for the unknown part when one part of two equal ratios is unknown

- Set up and solve proportions that arise in applications

- Recognize that constant growth in a table is related to proportional situations

- Connect a unit rate to the equation describing a situation

Developing Students' Mathematical Habits

The overall goal of the *Connected Mathematics* curriculum is to help students develop sound mathematical habits. Through their work in this and other number units, students learn important questions to ask themselves about situations that can be modeled mathematically.

- *When quantities have different measurements, how can they be compared?*

- *When can a comparison be made by subtraction?*

- *When can division be used?*

- *Why is a ratio a good means of comparison?*

- *How can a ratio be scaled up or down?*

- *How does rounding affect the numbers used in a ratio?*

- *What is the relationship between ratios and similar figures?*

- *How can ratios be used in daily life to find unknown quantities or inaccessible measurements?*

- *How can we use proportions to solve problems?*

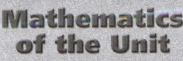

Mathematics of the Unit

Pearson Prentice Hall Professional Development

Overview

Although quantitative problems can be solved simply by counting members of a set or by measuring, it is often necessary to make decisions that involve comparisons of counts or measurements. The basic step in this kind of thinking is developed in elementary grades when such comparisons are decided by finding which number is greater. However, more useful reasoning often requires more careful comparison— explaining how much greater one number is than another, not in an absolute sense, but in a relative sense. There are many standard ways to make such comparisons (for example, fractions, ratios, rates, differences, and percents). One of the fundamental goals of school mathematics, especially middle-grades mathematics, is to help students develop flexible understanding, skill, and disposition in using strategies for comparing quantities. This goal runs throughout the Problems, ACE, and Reflections of this unit. The unit confronts students with a series of mathematical tasks that encourage them to make decisions about the quantities relevant to each task, how those quantities can be compared most usefully, and what information is provided by various quantitative comparisons.

The second major theme of this unit, as the title suggests, is *scaling*. In its most familiar sense, scaling suggests making something bigger or smaller, but similar in key respects to an original. Ratios and fractions often express comparative information in scaled-down form. For example, if a class consists of 15 boys and 10 girls, we might say that the ratio of boys to girls is 3 to 2, or that $\frac{3}{5}$ of the class is boys. We could also say that 60% of the class is boys, a kind of scaling up. *Stretching and Shrinking* lays a solid foundation of visual imagery to support the basic notion of scaling.

Research on students' understanding of proportional reasoning shows that moving from additive reasoning to multiplicative reasoning is difficult for students. Having experiences with geometric instances of proportional reasoning before concentrating on more numerical situations helps students in two ways: it gives students concrete experiences with visual representation of ratio comparisons, and it begins the work of

helping students see the difference between reasoning by taking differences and reasoning by comparing ratios. This is why *Stretching and Shrinking* is in the CMP curriculum before *Comparing and Scaling*. The idea of ratio comparison was introduced there, along with informal ideas of equivalent ratios. These ideas are extended in the current unit. In *Moving Straight Ahead*, students will see proportional reasoning related to linear equations that pass through the origin.

In *Stretching and Shrinking*, the problem was finding dimensions of a larger (or smaller) physical or graphical model while preserving the relative size of the component parts so that the figures remained mathematically similar. The same ideas and ways of thinking developed in *Stretching and Shrinking* become powerful ways of thinking about ratios. The goal is the same in many ratio situations—to scale a pair of ratios up or down to determine whether they are equal.

A comparison problem in *Stretching and Shrinking* that called for finding the missing part of a ratio equivalent to a given ratio is the same as solving a proportion in *Comparing and Scaling*. For example, suppose you have a rectangle with dimensions of 5 cm by 7 cm. You want to draw a larger, similar, rectangle with the side corresponding to 5 cm being 15 cm. What would the other dimension be? This is an identical question: If roses are 5 for $7, how much will 15 roses cost? In each case, we are dealing with the given ratio of 5 to 7 and looking for the equivalent ratio of 15 to x. *Stretching and Shrinking* precedes *Comparing and Scaling* to give students experience with these ideas in a more concrete geometric context.

To summarize, the broad purposes of this unit are twofold. First, to develop students' ability to make intelligent comparisons of quantitative information using ratios, fractions, decimals, rates, unit rates, and percents. Second, to use quantitative comparison information to make larger or smaller scale models or scale rates and ratios up and down. An additional goal of this unit is to have students not only learn different ways to reason in proportional situations, but to recognize when such reasoning is appropriate.

Many important mathematical applications involve comparing quantities of one kind or another. In some cases, the problem is simply deciding which of two quantities is greater and describing how much greater it is. In such instances, we subtract to find a difference. This is what students deal with in elementary school. In fact, comparison by addition or subtraction comes first in students' mathematics experiences. This way of thinking becomes inappropriately pervasive in any situation requiring comparison.

Summary of Investigations

Investigation 1
Making Comparisons

Investigation 1 focuses on the language of comparisons and ratios in the context of advertising. Some content connects to questions asked of students in the sixth-grade work on percents and data analysis. Students learn what different kinds of comparative statements mean about the data that is given. They are asked to write comparative statements that describe data. Questions are asked that engage students in making comparisons and checking the accuracy of statements given. The important question of how you decide whether to use a difference, ratio, fraction, or percent to make a particular comparison is raised.

Investigation 2
Comparing Ratios, Percents, and Fractions

Investigation 2 builds on the variety of strategies for making comparisons—ratios, percents, and fractions—that arose in Investigation 1. The intent is to see how information in each of these forms provides the information needed to derive either of the other forms. Students investigate in more depth how ratios can be formed and scaled up or down to find equivalent ratios. This investigation more directly raises issues with comparison by finding differences.

Investigation 3
Comparing and Scaling Rates

Investigation 3 takes a specific focus on rates, scaling rates, and finding and interpreting unit

rates as strategies. The investigation looks at scaling in numerical contexts; the connection to such proportional reasoning problems in geometry is made in Investigation 4. Rate tables are introduced as a tool for using scaling rates as a strategy for comparison. Students are asked to draw rate tables. They are also asked to write rules or equations. The ideas of average speed and constant speed are used. Students explicitly learn to use unit rates and to write equations and rules based on unit rates. Problem 4 confronts students with the need to label rates and unit rates carefully. When you divide to find a unit rate, determining what the division gives you is essential to making the comparison. Here students look at the measurement labels for assistance in determining what the quotient means.

Investigation 4
Making Sense of Proportions

Investigation 4 helps students write and use proportions to solve problems and make comparisons. All of the problems in this investigation can be posed in classical  $\frac{a}{b} = \frac{x}{d}$ or $\frac{a}{b} = \frac{c}{x}$ form; yet, they are solved in a variety of equivalent ways. It is important that students learn different ways to reason in proportional situations, and recognize *when* such reasoning is appropriate. The strategies used to solve problems are based on students' knowledge of equivalent fractions. In one case, a geometric context ties to earlier work. In Problem 4.3, we look more systematically for an efficient strategy for solving proportions. We do not, however, cover cross multiplication. We have made a commitment to help students make sense of the strategies they use and feel that efficiency is only effective if students truly make sense of what they are doing. Therefore, we focus on scaling ratios up and down as a way of solving proportions. This builds on the substantial foundation for understanding and using equivalent fractions in the sixth-grade curriculum.

Mathematics Background

The subtitle of *Comparing and Scaling* is *Ratio, Proportion, and Percent*. This subtitle makes clear that the heart of the unit goals is to recognize when making comparisons using these strategies is appropriate, then to use these strategies with understanding and efficiency.

Scaling Ratios as a Strategy

To compare two or more related measures or counts, such as 3 roses for $5 and 7 roses for $9, you need strategies that allow the related pairs of numbers to be compared. Simple subtraction will not tell you what you want to know. Enter the world of ratio and proportion. A proportion is a statement of equality between two ratios. In this example, you need to find a way to scale the ratios of 3 to 5 and 7 to 9 so that they can be directly compared. Many students think these two ratios are the same, reasoning that 4 has been added to each of the numbers 3 and 5 to get 7 and 9. This is an example of students' misconceptions about when additive comparisons are appropriate. If you appropriately scale both ratios so that either the number of roses or the costs are the same, you are then left with a simple comparison of the quantities that are not the same. The two possibilities are shown below.

If you want to scale the costs to be the same, the kind of thinking is the same as that for finding a common denominator: look for a number that represents a multiple of the two numbers 5 and 9. If you scale to make the prices the same (that is, $45), then the answer is immediately obvious.

$$\frac{3}{5} = \frac{3 \times 9}{5 \times 9} = \frac{27}{45} \text{ and } \frac{7}{9} = \frac{7 \times 5}{9 \times 5} = \frac{35}{45}$$

You can now compare the ratios 27 roses for $45 and 35 roses for $45. Clearly the second option gives more for the same amount of money.

Let's scale the numerators to be the same.

$$\frac{3}{5} = \frac{3 \times 7}{5 \times 7} = \frac{21}{35} \text{ and } \frac{7}{9} = \frac{7 \times 3}{9 \times 3} = \frac{21}{27}$$

You can now compare the ratios 21 roses for $35 and 21 roses for $27. Again the best buy is obvious.

This example underscores the relationship between the mathematical thinking used to find common denominators or common numerators in work with equivalent fractions and that was used to find equivalent ratios. Ratios are written in several forms. Some of the most often used are 2 to 3, or 2 : 3, or $\frac{2}{3}$. In the example, the convenience of writing the ratios as fractions helps the thinking needed for scaling the ratios up. However, we must make sure that students can differentiate between a ratio written as a fraction and a fraction representing the fractional part of a whole. We address this in the next section.

Using Ratio Statements to Find Fraction Statements of Comparison

The statement "the ratio of girls to boys in a class is 15 girls to 9 boys" can be written as the fraction $\frac{15}{9}$, but it does not mean that the fraction of students in the class that are girls is $\frac{15}{9}$. This is confusing for students and leads some teachers to avoid the fraction form for writing a ratio. We have chosen to confront the confusion by asking the fraction question directly.

Maria says the fraction of the class that is girls is $\frac{15}{9}$. Bob says the fraction of the class that is girls is $\frac{15}{24}$. Who is correct and why?

The correct answer hinges on recognizing that a new quantity is actually used to find the fraction of students in the class that are girls. The total number of students in the class is needed. This is the sum of the numbers of boys and girls, 24. The part to whole comparison is $\frac{15}{24}$, and Bob is correct. Now we turn to another strategy for solving the roses problem.

Per Quantities: Finding and Using Rates and Unit Rates

If you compute the price per rose, you will have a rate comparison for the roses problem. In the 3 for $5 deal, the unit rate is $1.67. The price per rose in the 7 for $9 deal is $1.29—clearly the better price. Alternatively, at the 3 for $5 price, 7 roses would cost $11.67. This is a different comparison with the same result. Let's explore this strategy a bit further.

Here are two ratios that suggest rates:

Sascha goes 5 miles in 20 minutes on the first part of his bike ride. On the second part, he goes 8 miles in 24 minutes. On which part is he riding faster?

Many students will intuitively want to divide the miles number and the minutes number to get a result, but they sometimes lose track of which one is divided into the other. Consequently they produce a number, but have no idea what the number means in the problem. Here the comparison can be made in two different ways by computing different unit rates. Let's look at each.

Suppose a student decided to divide 5 by 20 and 8 by 24. She gets the two numbers 0.25 and 0.333. What do these numbers mean? She might have divided 20 by 5 and 24 by 8. This division gives 4 and 3. What do these numbers mean? You have to know before you can decide what they tell us about the two legs of the bike ride. So start again and this time carry the label with the quantities.

$$\frac{5 \; miles}{20 \; minutes} = 0.25 \; miles \; per \; minute \; and$$

$$\frac{8 \; miles}{24 \; minutes} = 0.333 \ldots miles \; per \; minute$$

Now the comparison is clear. The times are the same, 1 minute, and the distances can be directly compared. 8 miles in 24 minutes is faster.

But, you could divide the other way:

$$\frac{20 \; minutes}{5 \; miles} = 4 \; minutes \; per \; mile \; and$$

$$\frac{24 \; minutes}{8 \; miles} = 3 \; minutes \; per \; mile$$

Now you see that the lesser number tells the correct answer, 8 miles in 24 minutes.

What makes unit rates so interesting, and somewhat difficult, for students is that you have two options when you divide two numbers. The units help students think through such situations with the goal of building the flexibility to use either set of unit rates to compare the quantities.

One of the recurring themes of these materials is that we can represent data in different ways and that each way may tell us something that is not as obvious from other representations. The comparison in the rose example can be made in several ways: for example, using unit rates, comparing the ratios in fraction form to determine which is greater, or scaling both rates until the price is the same or the number of roses is the same. Developing strategies for deciding what the comparison situation calls for and for making comparisons are major goals of this unit.

Relating Ratios, Fractions and Percents

It is often desirable to change one form of comparison statement to another. The question is, can you write a percent statement given either a ratio or a fraction statement, and can you write a ratio or fraction statement given a percent comparison statement? Let's explore this with an example.

The ratio of concentrate to water in a mix for lemonade is 3 cups concentrate to 16 cups water. The questions you might ask are: "What fraction of the lemonade will be concentrate?" or "What percent of the lemonade will be concentrate?"

First find the total cups the recipe makes. It makes 19 cups. Then write the fraction of the lemonade that is concentrate, $\frac{3}{19}$. Now finding the percent is easy. Just divide the concentrate by the total, $3 \div 19 = 0.15789 \ldots$ or about 15.8% concentrate.

Suppose you know that the percent of boys in a class is 48% and you want to write this as a ratio. You can think of the percent as a scaling of the ratio representing boys and girls up to a total of 100. So the girls are 52% of the class and the ratio of boys to girls is 48 to 52. You can scale this ratio down to 12 boys to 13 girls. The powerful thing about these related representations is the flexibility it gives us to choose the form of representation that describes the situation best for our purposes.

One caution about such changes of representation is that the choice to make these changes of form should be judged against whether the computations you do will have meaning. For example, in many rate situations, such as miles per gallon, trying to compute a percent does not make sense because the addition to get a total does not make sense. Miles covered plus gallons of gas used is a meaningless total. When the ratio can be thought of as part of a whole, the change of form we described makes sense (for example, white paint to blue paint in a mix, or high-fiber to high-protein nuggets in food for a baby chimp).

Proportions and Proportional Reasoning

The related concepts and skills in this unit are often referred to as *proportional reasoning*. Forming ratios in order to make comparisons is the heart of proportional reasoning. What is a proportion? A proportion is simply a statement of equality between two ratios. What makes this idea powerful is that if we know a ratio is equivalent to another, but we do not know both terms of one of the ratios, we can use what we already know about scaling or finding equivalent fractions to find the missing part of a proportion. Again, let's look at an example.

It takes Glenda 70 steps on the elliptical machine to go 0.1 mile. When her workout is done, she has gone 3 miles. How many steps has she taken on the machine?

Here is a proportion and a solution for the number of steps that Glenda made.

$$\frac{70 \; steps}{0.1 \; miles} = \frac{x \; steps}{3 \; miles} = \frac{70 \times 30 \; steps}{0.1 \times 30 \; miles} = \frac{2{,}100 \; steps}{3 \; miles}$$

The first ratio in the proportion is scaled up by multiplying both the numerator and the denominator by 30. Thus, the denominator equals the denominator of the ratio with the unknown, x. This allows us to read the value of x directly since we know that if the two fractions are equivalent and have the same denominator, the numerators are also the same. The strategy we use to find the number by which we multiply, or "scale," is the same as the thinking process we use to find common denominators for fractions.

How far you go in formalizing the solving of proportions will depend on you and your students. We highly recommend that you do not impose solution strategies that have no meaning for the students. While cross multiplication is efficient, for most students at this level it is used without any understanding of why it works and consequently is often misused. We believe that students are better served by having the time to learn to think through situations requiring solving proportions and develop flexibility in approaching a problem so that easy possible solution strategies are not missed in a rush to an algorithm. This approach also builds on mathematics students already know and ways of thinking that they have already acquired. Helping students want to make sense of mathematics is encouraging a kind of thinking and flexibility that will allow them to feel confident to tackle problems that do not look exactly like ones they have already solved. Part of the goal of this unit is for students to learn to make judgments about the situation and to choose methods for comparing and for scaling.

Cross-Multiplying

If someone mentions cross-multiplication and the students seem interested, don't just give a procedure for cross-multiplication. Develop the idea based on what your students already know—finding common denominators. (If we use the product of the original denominators as a common denominator, the numerators will be cross products). In Question C part (2) of Problem 4.1, $\frac{7}{12} = \frac{x}{9}$, the common denominator will be 108. In the first fraction we have to multiply the numerator and denominator by 9. In the second fraction we need to multiply the numerator and the denominator by 12 to make the denominators the same.

Because the denominators are now the same, we need to find the value of x that makes the numerators equal. So we have to find x when $12x = 63$. This means that x must be 5.25. $\frac{7}{12} = \frac{x}{9}$ is equivalent to $\frac{63}{108} = \frac{12x}{108}$ is equivalent to $63 = 12x$, therefore $x = 5.25$.

So in a sense, cross-multiplying asks the question: What would be the numerator if these two fractions had a particular common denominator (the product of the original denominators)?

Helping students to make their own reasoning explicit can lead to a generalized method of solving proportions. For example, when many students solve this proportion $\frac{3}{7} = \frac{x}{343}$, they do the following arithmetic.

$$(343 \div 7) \times 3 = \frac{343}{7} \times 3 = \frac{343 \times 3}{7}$$

The division $343 \div 7$ finds the scaling factor by which we need to scale the 3.

Consequently, for solving a general proportion $\frac{a}{b} = \frac{x}{c}$, we can follow the same reasoning: find the scaling factor by computing $c \div b$, then multiply the scaling factor by a. So the arithmetic we actually perform is scale factor $\times$ the known numerator. In symbols this is $\frac{c}{b} \times a = x$ or $\frac{c \times a}{b} = x$.

With the unknown in the denominator, find the scale factor using the numerators so that we can scale the denominators to find the unknown. To solve $\frac{a}{b} = \frac{c}{x}$, we first find the scale factor by which we can make the numerators the same, $c \div a$. Then we have to scale the denominator to see what is equal to x. This gives $\frac{c}{a} \times b = x$ or $\frac{c \times b}{a} = x$.

An alternative strategy can be built using fact family ideas. To solve $\frac{a}{b} = \frac{c}{x}$, think of the equation as $\frac{a}{b} = c \div x$. From fact families, we can say that $x = c \div \frac{a}{b}$. Rewriting the right side with common denominators gives $x = \frac{cb}{b} \div \frac{a}{b} = cb \div a$, or $x = \frac{cb}{a}$.

These are the equations we would get by cross-multiplication, but here the explanation is built on students' ways of reasoning.

Big Idea	Prior Work	Future Work
Ratio as a proportional relationship between quantities	Exploring and applying rational number concepts (*Bits and Pieces I, II, and III*)	Calculating and applying slope in equations of $y = mx + b$ form (*Moving Straight Ahead, Thinking With Mathematical Models, Say It With Symbols*)
Percent as a proportion that is always compared to 100	Percent defined as a ratio to 100 and connected to fractions and decimals (*Bits and Pieces I, II, and III*)	Making comparisons between groups of different sizes (*Data Around Us ©2004, Samples and Populations*)
Fractions as a ratio, rate, or as a part/whole relation	Fractions as a part/whole comparison; addition, subtraction, multiplication, and division with fractions (*Bits and Pieces I & II, How Likely Is It?*)	Expressing and applying probabilities as fractions (*What Do You Expect?*), determining if two algebraic expressions are equivalent (*Say It With Symbols*)
Scaling to determine one quantity in terms of another and to find equivalent ratios	Comparing and subdividing similar figures to determine scale factors (*Stretching and Shrinking*)	Scaling up rectangular prisms (*Filling and Wrapping*)
Comparing quantities using ratios, proportions, rates, or percents	Connecting and comparing rates using ratios, decimals, and percents (*Bits and Pieces I & II*), comparing data sets (*Data About Us*)	Comparing probabilities (*What Do You Expect?, Samples and Populations*), comparing data sets (*Data Around Us ©2004*)
Developing strategies and techniques to solve for missing values in a proportion	Making inferences about quantities and populations based on experimental or theoretical probabilities (*How Likely Is It?*)	Developing benchmarks and skills for estimating irrational numbers (*Looking for Pythagoras*), estimating populations (*Samples and Populations*), estimating with and comparing large numbers (*Data Around Us ©2004*)

Planning for the Unit

Pacing Suggestions and Materials

Investigations and Assessments	Pacing 45–50 min. classes	Materials for Students	Materials for Teachers
1 Making Comparisons	3 days		Product ads that involve comparisons (optional); Transparencies 1.1A, 1.1B, 1.3; chart paper (optional)
Mathematical Reflections	$\frac{1}{2}$ day		
2 Comparing Ratios, Percents, and Fractions	4 days		Transparencies 2.2, 2.3A, 2.3B
Mathematical Reflections	$\frac{1}{2}$ day		
Assessment: Check Up	$\frac{1}{2}$ day		
3 Comparing and Scaling Rates	4 days	Graphing calculators, grid paper	Transparencies 3.1A, 3.1B, 3.4A, 3.4B
Mathematical Reflections	$\frac{1}{2}$ day		
Assessment: Partner Quiz	1 day		
4 Making Sense of Proportions	4 days	Labsheets 4ACE Exercise 27a and 4ACE Exercise 27b, graphing calculators	Transparencies 4.1A, 4.1B
Mathematical Reflections	$\frac{1}{2}$ day		
Looking Back and Looking Ahead	$\frac{1}{2}$ day		
Assessment: Unit Project	Optional	Labsheets Student's Guide, Paper Pool A–C	
Assessment: Self Assessment	Take Home		
Assessment: Unit Test	1 day		

Total Time	**20 days**	**Materials for Use in All Investigations**	
For detailed pacing for Problems within each Investigation, see the Suggested Pacing at the beginning of each Investigation. For pacing with block scheduling, see next page.		Calculators, blank transparencies and transparency markers (optional), chart paper and markers (optional), student notebooks	Blank transparencies and transparency markers (optional)

Pacing for Block Scheduling (90-minute class periods)

Investigation	Suggested Pacing	Investigation	Suggested Pacing
Investigation 1	**2 days**	**Investigation 3**	**$2\frac{1}{2}$ days**
Problem 1.1	$\frac{1}{2}$ day	Problem 3.1	$\frac{1}{2}$ day
Problem 1.2	$\frac{1}{2}$ day	Problem 3.2	$\frac{1}{2}$ day
Problem 1.3	$\frac{1}{2}$ day	Problem 3.3	$\frac{1}{2}$ day
Math Reflections	$\frac{1}{2}$ day	Problem 3.4	$\frac{1}{2}$ day
Investigation 2	**$2\frac{1}{2}$ days**	Math Reflections	$\frac{1}{2}$ day
Problem 2.1	$\frac{1}{2}$ day	**Investigation 4**	**$2\frac{1}{2}$ days**
Problem 2.2	$\frac{1}{2}$ day	Problem 4.1	1 day
Problem 2.3	1 day	Problem 4.2	$\frac{1}{2}$ day
Math Reflections	$\frac{1}{2}$ day	Problem 4.3	$\frac{1}{2}$ day
		Math Reflections	$\frac{1}{2}$ day

Vocabulary

Essential Terms Developed in This Unit	Useful Terms Referenced in This Unit	Terms Developed in Previous Units
rate ratio proportion unit rate	rate table	average compare data decimal denominator dependent difference equation equivalence fraction graph/coordinate graph independent mean percent scale/scaling factor/scale factor variables

Program Resources

For: Teacher Resources
Web Code: ank–5500

Components

Use the chart below to quickly see which components are available for each Investigation.

Investigation	Labsheets	Additional Practice	Transparencies		Formal Assessment		Assessment Options	
			Problem	Summary	Check Up	Partner Quiz	Multiple-Choice	Question Bank
1		✔	1.1A, 1.1B, 1.3	1.1			✔	✔
2		✔	2.2, 2.3A, 2.3B		✔		✔	✔
3		✔	3.1A, 3.1B, 3.4A, 3.4B			✔	✔	✔
4	4ACE Exercise 27a and 27b	✔	4.1A, 4.1B, 4.2				✔	✔
Unit Project	Student's Guide, Paper Pool A–C							
For the Unit	Grid paper	*ExamView* CD-ROM, Web site			Unit Test, Unit Project, Notebook Check, Self Assessment		Multiple-Choice, Question Bank, *ExamView* CD-ROM	

Also Available For Use With This Unit
- Parent Guide: take-home letter for the unit
- Implementing CMP
- Spanish Assessment Resources
- Additional online and technology resources

Technology

The Use of Calculators

Connected Mathematics was developed with the belief that calculators should be available and that students should learn when their use is appropriate. For this reason, we do not designate specific problems as "calculator problems." The calculations in *Comparing and Scaling* involve only simple arithmetic, so nonscientific calculators are adequate.

Student Interactivity CD-ROM

Includes interactive versions of Scaling Figures and Paper Pool. Also available online at PHSchool.com, Web Code ank-5500.

PHSchool.com

For Students Multiple-choice practice with instant feedback, updated data sources, data sets for Tinkerplots data software.

For Teachers Professional development, curriculum support, downloadable forms, and more.

See also www.math.msu.edu/cmp for more resources for both teachers and students.

ExamView® CD-ROM

Create multiple versions of practice sheets and tests for course objectives and standardized tests. Includes dynamic questions, online testing, student reports, and all test and practice items in Spanish. Also includes all items in the *Assessment Resources* and *Additional Practice*.

Teacher Express™ CD-ROM

Includes a lesson planning tool, the Teacher's Guide pages, and all the teaching resources.

LessonLab Online Courses

LessonLab offers comprehensive, facilitated professional development designed to help teachers implement CMP2 and improve student achievement. To learn more, please visit PHSchool.com/cmp2.

Assessment Summary

Ongoing Informal Assessment

Embedded in the Student Unit

Problems Use students' work from the Problems to check student understanding.

ACE exercises Use ACE exercises for homework assignments to assess student understanding.

Mathematical Reflections Have students summarize their learning at the end of each Investigation.

Looking Back and Looking Ahead At the end of the unit, use the first two sections to allow students to show what they know about the unit.

Additional Resources

Teacher's Guide Use the Check for Understanding feature of some Summaries and the probing questions that appear in the *Launch, Explore,* or *Summarize* sections of all Investigations to check student understanding.

Summary Transparencies Use these transparencies to focus class attention on a summary check for understanding.

Self Assessment

Notebook Check Students use this tool to organize and check their notebooks before giving them to their teacher. Located in *Assessment Resources*.

Self Assessment At the end of the unit, students reflect on and provide examples of what they learned. Located in *Assessment Resources*.

Formal Assessment

Choose the assessment materials that are appropriate for your students.

Assessment	For Use After	Focus	Student Work
Check Up	Invest. 2	Skills	Individual
Partner Quiz	Invest. 3	Rich problems	Pair
Unit Test	The Unit	Skills, rich problems	Individual
Unit Project	The Unit	Rich problems	Individual

Additional Resources

Multiple-Choice Items Use these items for homework, review, a quiz, or add them to the Unit Test.

Question Bank Choose from these questions for homework, review, or replacements for Quiz, Check Up, or Unit Test questions.

Additional Practice Choose practice exercises for each Investigation for homework, review, or formal assessments.

***ExamView* CD-ROM** Create practice sheets, review quizzes, and tests with this dynamic software. Give online tests and receive student progress reports. *(All test items are also available in Spanish.)*

Spanish Assessment Resources

Includes Partner Quizzes, Check Ups, Unit Test, Multiple-Choice Items, Question Bank, Notebook Check, and Self Assessment. Plus, the *ExamView* CD-ROM has all test items in Spanish.

Correlation to Standardized Tests

Investigation	NAEP	Terra Nova		ITBS	SAT10	Local Test
		CAT6	CTBS			
1 Making Comparisons	N1e, N3a, N4a	✔	✔		✔	
2 Comparing Ratios, Percents, and Fractions	N4b, N4c, N5f	✔	✔		✔	
3 Comparing and Scaling Rates	M1l, A1a, A2a	✔	✔		✔	
4 Making Sense of Proportions	N1d, M1k, A4b	✔	✔		✔	

NAEP National Assessment of Educational Progress

CAT6/Terra Nova California Achievement Test, 6th Ed.
CTBS/Terra Nova Comprehensive Test of Basic Skills

ITBS Iowa Test of Basic Skills, Form M
SAT10 Stanford Achievement Test, 10th Ed.

Comparing and Scaling

Ratio, Proportion, and Percent

Glenda Lappan

James T. Fey

William M. Fitzgerald

Susan N. Friel

Elizabeth Difanis Phillips

PEARSON

Boston, Massachusetts · Glenview, Illinois · Shoreview, Minnesota · Upper Saddle River, New Jersey

STUDENT PAGE

Notes

_____

_____

_____

_____

(1) 12

Comparing and Scaling

At camp, Miriam uses a pottery wheel to make 3 bowls in 2 hours. Duane makes 5 bowls in 3 hours. Who is the faster potter? Suppose they continue to work at the same pace. How long will it take each of them to make a set of 12 bowls?

It takes 100 maple trees to make 25 gallons of maple syrup. How many maple trees does it take for one gallon of syrup?

Two summers ago, a biologist captured, tagged, and released 20 puffins on an island. When she returned this past summer, she captured 50 puffins. Two of them were tagged. About how many puffins are on the island?

2 Comparing and Scaling

Notes _____

_____

_____

_____

Many everyday problems and decisions call for comparisons. Which car is safer? Which horse is the fastest? Which Internet service is cheaper? In some cases, the comparisons involve only counting, measuring, or rating, then ordering the results from least to greatest. In other cases, more complex reasoning is required.

How would you answer the comparison questions on the previous page?

In this unit, you will explore many ways to compare numbers. You'll learn how to both choose and use the best comparison strategies to solve problems and make decisions.

Notes

Mathematical Highlights

Ratio, Proportion, and Percent

In *Comparing and Scaling*, you will develop several methods for comparing quantities. You will use these methods to solve problems.

You will learn how to

- Use informal language to ask comparison questions

    Examples:

    "What is the ratio of boys to girls in our class?"

    "What fraction of the class is going to the spring picnic?"

    "What percent of the girls play basketball?"

    "Which model of car has the best fuel economy?"

- Choose an appropriate method to make comparisons among quantities using ratios, percents, fractions, rates, or differences

- Find equivalent forms of given ratios and rates to scale comparisons up and down

- Find and interpret unit rates, and use them to make comparisons

- Use unit rates to write an equation to represent a pattern in a table of data

- Set up and solve proportions

- Use proportional reasoning to solve problems

As you work on the problems in this unit, ask yourself questions about problem situations that involve comparisons:

What quantities should be compared?

What type of comparison will give the most useful information?

How can the comparison be expressed in different but useful ways?

How can given comparison data be used to make predictions about unknown quantities?

Notes _____

_____

_____

_____

Introducing Your Students to Comparing and Scaling

Previously, students have made comparisons of numbers by finding the difference between them. Such comparisons require only one corresponding measure from each of two or more situations. However, in many situations, more useful comparisons are made by using multiplication (or division) strategies rather than addition (or subtraction) strategies. When pizza is shared, for example, both the number of pizzas and the number of people are factors in determining how much pizza each person will get. "Pizzas per person" is a kind of ratio called a *rate*. A rate is based on two measures, and the underlying operation is multiplication (division). This unit introduces students to situations in which comparisons are needed. Students learn that multiplicative comparisons using ratios is a form of proportional reasoning.

Using the Unit Opener

Discuss with your students the three questions posed on the opening page of the Student Edition. The problems will be answered within the unit, so students are not expected to solve them here. Raise these questions to see what students spontaneously come up with, not to teach solution strategies. This should give you an idea of how advanced they are in proportional reasoning already. Take a few minutes to allow student ideas with the goal of generating enthusiasm for the kinds of situations in the unit.

Extend students' thinking with these questions:

- *How could you use fractions to express the data?*

- *How could you use percents to express the data?*

Summarize by explaining the following:

- *The questions we have just discussed are similar to many that occur in other situations. The unit we are starting will help you develop your skill in thinking about these kinds of problems. You will see that many of the mathematical ideas and skills you are already familiar with—fractions, decimals, percents, rates, and even tables, graphs, and algebraic equations—can be used to help solve problems that involve making comparisons.*

Using the Mathematical Highlights

The Mathematical Highlights page in the Student Edition provides information to students, parents, and other family members. It gives students a preview of the mathematics and some of the overarching questions that they should ask themselves while studying *Comparing and Scaling*.

As they work through the unit, students can refer to the Mathematical Highlights page to review what they have learned and to preview what is still to come. This page also tells students' families what mathematical ideas and activities will be covered as the class works through *Comparing and Scaling*.

Using the Unit Project

As a final assessment in *Comparing and Scaling*, you may administer the Unit Test or assign the Unit Project, Paper Pool. This optional unit project provides students an opportunity to further develop their understanding of ratio and proportion. It also connects to and uses geometric similarity as students studied in *Stretching and Shrinking*. The project is formally assigned near the end of the unit.

We recommend that students work on the project with a partner. Allow one class period for pairs to collect their data. They can continue to investigate the task and draft their reports outside of class. Part of a second class period could be used for comparing results and finalizing reports. You may have students share their results in a class summary of the project.

A scoring rubric and samples of student work are given on pages 94–98 of the Guide to the Unit Project.

Investigation 1 Making Comparisons

Mathematical and Problem-Solving Goals

- Informally explore various strategies for presenting quantitative comparison information
- Use the language of ratios
- Make judgments and choices on given comparative statements about quantities
- Analyze and create comparison statements from given data

Summary of Problems

Problem 1.1 Ads That Sell

Students informally explore strategies for presenting quantitative comparison information. The language of ratios is introduced through the phrasing of comparisons that are typical of advertisements. However, comparisons by differences and by percents are also included so that students can begin to make judgments about what kind of comparison makes the most sense in a given situation.

Problem 1.2 Targeting an Audience

Students explore another set of survey data and analyze a set of statements to build on what they learned in Problem 1.1. Students analyze statements from different points of view.

Problem 1.3 American Records

This problem provides data on some of the largest living trees as well as data on the tallest man and the typical height, waist measure, and arm span for a group of adult males. Students are asked to compose statements that make comparisons between the trees in the table and the data given on human males. Analyzing and composing are different levels of understanding, and this problem is key in the process of helping students become skillful at both.

	Suggested Pacing	Materials for Students	Materials for Teachers	ACE Assignments
All	$3\frac{1}{2}$ days	Calculators, student notebooks	Blank transparencies and transparency markers (optional)	
1.1	1 day		Product ads that involve comparisons (optional), Transparencies 1.1A and 1.1B	1–3, 11–16, 34
1.2	1 day			4–7, 17–33, 35
1.3	1 day		Transparency 1.3, chart paper and markers (optional)	8–10, 36–41
MR	$\frac{1}{2}$ day			

1.1 Ads That Sell

Goals

- Informally explore various strategies for presenting quantitative comparison information

- Use the language of ratios

The language of ratios is introduced as simply a way of phrasing comparisons. The setting is typical of preference data from advertisements. Students are likely to be familiar with advertisements such as these. Be sure to keep the conversation at the exploration level. Different kinds of ratio comparisons and ways of representing the comparison (fractions, ratios, rates, and percents) surface in the problem. Each of these will be developed more fully in later problems.

Launch 1.1

Suggested Questions You may start this problem by asking the students about their experiences with advertisements.

- *Can you think of any commercials that compare one product to another or several others?*

- *Can you think of any that involve a comparison using numbers?*

You may want to bring in a product ad that involves such a comparison of numbers. Take stock of the comparison types with which students are most familiar.

Turn to the four ways of presenting data from the cola trials. Read them with your students.

Suggested Questions Challenge them to discuss in groups questions such as:

- *What do you know from each form of comparison given?*

- *What information is missing from each form of comparison?*

- *Is each form of comparison accurate and effective?*

View these discussions as setting the scene for the exploration and the summary. Do not press

too hard for the students to come up with good answers. The intent is to plant these kinds of questions in their heads as they begin their work on the problem. Students may see that, in the 3-to-2 comparison, you lose any sense of how many people were in the trials, but you can immediately get a sense of the comparison. Out of every five people in the trials, three liked Bolda Cola better. This latter point is one to push in the summary as some students will have difficulty realizing that 3 to 2 means 3 out of 5 and 2 out of 5.

A small group arrangement works well.

Explore 1.1

This problem is meant to raise issues that will be studied in more detail in the unit. Even so, be on the lookout for students who are having trouble moving beyond finding differences as *the* method of comparison. You will need to pay particular attention to these students as the unit progresses.

As you move from group to group, look for good explanations or insights about what each form of comparison does and does not provide. This activity should set the stage for the kinds of questions students should ask themselves as they solve problems by making comparisons.

Going Further

- *From the statement, "People prefer Bolda Cola over Cola Nola by a ratio of 3 to 2," can you tell what fraction of those surveyed preferred Bolda Cola?* ($\frac{3}{5}$, or 3 out of 5 prefer Bolda Cola.)

Summarize 1.1

As a class, discuss what the groups found. The common language used in making comparisons should, in this problem, be examined through the lens of mathematics. For each form of comparison, write on the overhead what it tells and what it does not tell about the newspaper ad. Be sure students see that some of the statements lose the original data and some preserve the data.

However, some forms are easy to visualize and others are not. Again, this problem is for raising issues and reviewing everyday ways of making comparisons.

Suggested Questions Here are some questions that will be useful in the Summary:

- *From the first statement, can you tell how many people took the taste test?* (Yes, 28,565 people took the taste test.)

- *If you had only this statement, would you have a good sense of the strength of the preference for Bolda Cola? If not, what would you do with the statement to make it tell a better story about the test?* (Many will say no and suggest finding the difference. If so, then go directly to Statement 2.)

- *How is Statement 2 related to Statement 1?* (It is the difference between those that preferred Bolda Cola and those that preferred Cola Nola.)

- *If you did not have Statement 1, just Statement 2, could you tell how many people took the survey?* (No.)

- *Does this statement give you a sense of the strength of preference?* (This depends on the number taking the survey. If 15,000 took the survey, this is a real difference. If 500,000 took the survey, this is not much of a difference.)

- *Does knowing that 60% preferred Bolda Cola give a good sense of the comparison?* (Yes. This percentage tells you the comparison regardless of the number taking the survey. However, you do have to worry about whether the sample is representative of the entire population.)

- *Do you know from this statement how many were surveyed?* (No.)

- *Do you know from the 3 to 2 statement how many were surveyed?* (No.)

- *How are the 60% and the 3 to 2 statement related?* (60% means that 40% preferred the other cola. 60 to 40 is the same thing as 3 to 2.)

Discuss the Going Further question from the Explore section.

Transparency 1.1B

To push students to think a bit more about comparison statements, use the situations and questions that are posed on Transparency 1.1B.

A school counselor considered several different ways to report on the seventh-grade class:

The seventh-grade class in Neilson Middle School has more girls than boys.

- *"The ratio of girls to boys is 5 to 4."*
- *"Girls comprise about 56% of the class."*
- *"Four ninths of the class members are boys."*

1. *What does the word "ratio" mean?* (A ratio of 5 to 4 means that for every 5 girls in the class, there are 4 boys.)

2. *What does "56% of the class" mean?* (56% means that if there were 100 students in the class, 56 of them would be girls.)

3. *What does "four ninths of the class" mean?* (Four ninths means that out of every 9 students in the class, 4 are boys.)

4. *Could the counselor's statements all be correct? Why or why not?* (Yes, they are all equivalent statements. A ratio of 5 girls to 4 boys means that 4 out of 9 students are boys and 5 out of 9 students are girls. Five ninths is equivalent to $55.\overline{5}\%$, or about 56%.)

5. *Can you tell how many students were in the class? Why or why not?* (No, none of the statements tells you the exact number of girls, boys, or total students.)

Ads That Sell

Mathematical Goals

- Informally explore various strategies for presenting quantitative comparison information
- Use the language of ratios

Launch

Consider asking:

- *Can you think of any commercials that compare one product to another or several others?*
- *Can you think of any that involve a comparison using numbers?*

Consider bringing in an ad that involves comparison.

Challenge students to discuss in groups these questions that relate to the data from the cola trials:

- *What do you know from each form of comparison given?*
- *What information is missing from each form of comparison?*
- *Is each form of representation accurate and effective?*

Materials

- Product ads that involve comparisons (optional)
- Transparency 1.1A

Vocabulary

- ratio

Explore

Be on the lookout for students having trouble moving beyond finding differences.

Going Further

- *From the statement, "People prefer Bolda Cola over Cola Nola by a ratio of 3 to 2," can you tell what fraction of those surveyed preferred Bolda Cola?*

Summarize

Discuss as a class the group findings.

Consider asking:

- *From the first statement, can you tell how many people took the taste test?*
- *If you had only this statement, would you have a good sense of the strength of the preference for Bolda Cola? If not, what would you do with the statement to make it tell a better story?*
- *How is Statement 2 related to Statement 1?*
- *If you did not have Statement 1, just Statement 2, could you tell how many people took the survey?*
- *Does this statement give you a sense of the strength of preference?*
- *Does knowing that 60% preferred Bolda Cola give a good sense of the comparison?*

Materials

- Transparency 1.1B
- Transparency markers (optional)
- Student notebooks

continued on next page

- *Do you know from this statement how many were surveyed?*
- *Do you know from the 3 to 2 statement how many were surveyed?*
- *How are the 60% and the 3 to 2 statement related?*

Use Summary Transparency 1.1 as a quick check for understanding.

ACE Assignment Guide for Problem 1.1

Differentiated Instruction
Solutions for All Learners

Core 1, 2, 34
Other *Applications* 3; *Connections* 11–16

Adapted For suggestions about adapting Exercise 1 and other ACE exercises, see the CMP *Special Needs Handbook*.
Connecting to Prior Units 11, 12: *Bits and Pieces I, Bits and Pieces II*; 13–16: *Stretching and Shrinking*

Answers to Problem 1.1

Answers will vary in Questions A–E, but we suggest some of the following guides to what you might expect and/or push for in the discussion.

A. Statement 1 means that out of the total number surveyed (17,139 + 11,426 = 28,565), 17,139 of them preferred Bolda Cola and 11,426 preferred Cola Nola. In other words, for every 17,139 people who preferred Bolda Cola, there were 11,426 who preferred Cola Nola. Statement 2 reports the difference in numbers between the two groups of people. We can't tell how many people were surveyed, but we do know that 5,713 more people preferred Bolda Cola. Statement 3 means that 60 percent (60%) of the sample chose Bolda Cola as their preference. 60% means that if there were 100 people, 60 would prefer Bolda Cola. Statement 4 means that for every 3 people who preferred Bolda Cola, there were 2 people who preferred Cola Nola.

B. The ratio 3 to 2 or the 60% might be the most effective advertisements because the numbers are smaller and easier to relate to. You can easily use the ratio of 3 to 2 to predict what you would expect preferences to be in your class or in some other group of people. Or, the greater numbers may make a more powerful impression; the difference between 3 and 2 is only 1, while the difference between 17,139 and 11,426 is 5,713.

C. Yes, it is possible. The ratio of 17,139 to 11,426 (which have a difference of 5,713) can be approximated as 3 to 2, which is equivalent to 60% of the people surveyed choosing Bolda Cola over Cola Nola. Notice that $60\% = \frac{3}{5}$, not $\frac{3}{2}$. It is important to keep asking whether we are comparing part-to-part or part-to-whole in a given situation.

D. 1.5 times as many people preferred Bolda Cola to Cola Nola. $\frac{3}{5}$ (three fifths) of people surveyed preferred Bolda Cola.

E. 600 would prefer Bolda Cola, and 400 would prefer Cola Nola. 60% of 1,000 is 600, and 1,000 − 600 = 400.

1.2 Targeting an Audience

Goal

- Make judgments and choices on given comparative statements about quantities

Launch 1.2

Set the scene for the work by looking at the student edition note on ways to write ratios.

- *As you work on comparison problems, you will see that ratio is a very important kind of comparison. You might have seen statements of ratios written in different ways. Let's look at three common ways ratios are written.*

Now look at the text in the Student Edition. Make the point about what fractions usually mean and what they mean in a ratio context. Ratios represented as fractions are very useful as they invoke the understanding that students have built about finding and using equivalent fractions. Students learn to use the context to determine when ratios need to be treated as fractions for the purpose of finding equivalent ratios and when fractions have a different meaning (part-to-whole).

Introduce the problem by reading the information about advertisers with the class. Discuss the setting for the problem. Emphasize that 150 Neilson Middle School students were surveyed about their preferences, and that six ways of comparing the data are given in the problem. You may want to read the six statements as a class. Leave discussion of the statements for the groups.

Use a Think-Pair-Share grouping for this problem.

Explore 1.2

When you feel the class understands the problem, have them examine each statement for accuracy and to answer the questions.

Suggested Questions As you circulate, look for groups who are struggling to make sense of the statements, and ask questions such as the following to help them sort out the information:

- *If one third of the students prefer radio to television, what fraction prefers television to radio?* ($\frac{2}{3}$)

- *Out of the 150 surveyed, how many preferred radio and how many preferred television?* (50 preferred radio, and 100 preferred television.)

- *Now write a ratio statement comparing those who prefer radio to those who prefer television.* (50 to 100)

- *What is another ratio that is equivalent to this one that is easier to use?* (1 to 2)

- *How did you find this ratio?* (Divided both 50 and 100 by the common factor of 50.)

- *How is this like finding an equivalent fraction?* ($\frac{50}{100}$ is equivalent to $\frac{1}{2}$ because we can divide both the numerator and the denominator by the common factor of 50 and keep the fraction equivalent.)

Listen for good arguments about why a statement is accurate and why some are more effective than others.

Going Further
If students finish early, ask them to write an accurate comparison that is different from those given.

Summarize 1.2

Ask groups to report on any statements that they initially disagreed about and say how they resolved their disagreements. If any disagreements remain, let individuals present their arguments to help the class decide what seems reasonable. As students explain how they concluded that each statement except Statement 6 was accurate, you can review alternate ways of explaining equivalent ratios. For Question C, ask groups to explain what they chose as the best way to express the comparison of preferences and to defend their choices.

INVESTIGATION 1

1.2 Targeting an Audience

Mathematical Goal

- Make judgments and choices on given comparative statements about quantities

Launch

Begin by discussing:

- *As you work on comparison problems, you will see that ratio is a very important kind of comparison. You might have seen statements of ratios written in different ways. Let's look at three common ways ratios are written.*

Make the point about what fractions usually mean and what they mean in a ratio context—part-to-whole usually means fraction, part-to-part usually means ratio.

Consider reading the six statements in Question B as a class to introduce the problem.

Use a Think-Pair-Share grouping.

Explore

For those struggling, consider asking:

- *If one third of the students prefer radio to television, what fraction prefers television to radio?*
- *Out of the 150 surveyed, how many preferred radio and how many preferred television?*
- *Now write a ratio statement comparing those who prefer radio to those who prefer television.*
- *What is another ratio that is equivalent to this one that is easier to use?*
- *How did you find this ratio?*
- *How is this like finding an equivalent fraction?*

Going Further

If students finish early, ask them to write an accurate comparison that is different from those given.

Summarize

Ask groups to report on any statements they initially disagreed about and say how they resolved them.

Review alternative ways of explaining equivalent ratios.

Materials
- Student notebooks

ACE Assignment Guide
for Problem 1.2

Differentiated Instruction
Solutions for All Learners

Core 4, 5, 7
Other *Applications* 6; *Connections* 17–33; *Extensions* 35; unassigned choices from previous problems

Adapted For suggestions about adapting ACE exercises, see the CMP *Special Needs Handbook*.
Connecting to Prior Units 17–21: *Shapes and Designs, How Likely Is It?*; 22–33: *Bits and Pieces I*

Answers to Problem 1.2

A. Some possible comparisons involve the use of ratio (for example, 100 television to 50 radio or 2 to 1) because you are comparing among the students. You are comparing the quantities of those who prefer television to those who prefer radio. Students could also say that the preferences could be compared by fractions. ($\frac{100}{150} = \frac{2}{3}$ prefer television versus $\frac{50}{150} = \frac{1}{3}$ prefer radio). Here are some other ways of thinking that might help some students who are struggling. You can think of 100 to 50 as 2 groups of 50 to 1 group of 50, as shown in this drawing.

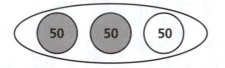

Then, 2 groups of 50 to 1 group of 50 could be thought of as 2 to 1. Percents could also be used: About 67% of students prefer watching television while about 33% prefer listening to the radio.

B. 1. Yes. The total number of students is 150, and $\frac{50}{150} = \frac{1}{3}$.
   2. Yes. 100 : 50 = 2 : 1
   3. Yes. 50 : 100 = 1 : 2
   4. Yes. 100 − 50 = 50. The problem discusses difference.
   5. Yes. 100 = 2 × 50
   6. No. About 33% of students prefer radio to television.

C. Statement 5 is more informative because it gives individuals a scale factor, whereas the difference is more dependent on the actual numbers. For example, the difference between 100 and 50 is more impressive than the difference between 1,000 and 950. A ratio is more informative in comparing these two quantities than the difference.

D. 1. Possible answer: Statement 1 because it frames the preference for radio in a positive light.
   2. Possible answer: Statement 5 because the scale factor of 2 (twice or doubled) sounds impressive.

Goal

- Analyze and create comparison statements from given data

This problem gives students three kinds of measures for some of the largest trees in America. Students are asked to check the statements given to determine whether the statements accurately reflect the data given. Then students are given additional data and asked to compose statements that make comparisons between the tree data and the new data. Note that this requires students to think in two directions—being the judge of statements of comparison and composing effective and accurate statements of comparison.

Launch 1.3

Ask if any of your students know any world records or facts about record holders. They may know sports facts or other kinds of strange world records. The point is to get them thinking about data around world records.

Read over the data table with your students and make sure they understand that the data given are measures recorded for some of the largest living trees.

Suggested Questions

- *What are some different ways that quantities can be written?* (Examples of responses: Quantities can be written as fractions or decimals. Percents are ways of expressing "out of 100," so they can be easily written as a decimal or a fraction.)

- *What different forms have we seen so far to express the same comparison?* (Fraction, percent, ratio, or sometimes difference.)

- *How is a ratio different from a percent and from a fraction?* (A ratio is a part-to-part comparison, and a fraction and a percent are part-to-whole comparisons.)

- *How can you express something written as a ratio as a fraction?* (You add the two ratio numbers to find the whole, and then express the fraction as the ratio number over the whole. For example, 5 to 7 means 5 out of 12, or $\frac{5}{12}$.)

- *Does it always make sense to add the two numbers in a situation to get a whole?* (No. Only if the two numbers can be thought of as parts of a whole representing the same kinds of things. For example, if we are comparing 80 miles for 2 gallons and 100 miles for 3 gallons, there is no "whole" since miles and gallons are different kinds of measures. Whereas with 80 girls to 20 boys, we can think of the whole as the mixed population of both boys and girls, then add the two counts to get a whole, 100 children.)

The first part of the problem will ask them to figure out whether the statements given are accurate. Remind them to prepare to justify their answers.

The second part of the problem gives data on the tallest man to have ever lived. Now the students will be the ones asked to write comparison statements between Wadlow and the largest living trees.

Suggested Questions To segue to the second part of the problem, you might want to ask the class to give some additional statements of comparison from the tree data.

- *What additional statements can you make to compare the giant sequoia to the Florida crossopetalum?* (Examples: The ratio of the height of the giant sequoia to the height of the Florida crossopetalum is 25 to 1. The giant sequoia is 264 feet taller than the Florida crossopetalum. The height of the Florida crossopetalum is 4% of the height of the giant sequoia.)

In Question C, data are given on an average man. Again students are asked to write comparison statements that use the ideas of fractions, ratios, percents, and differences. Question D asks students to think about how they decide which form of comparison makes sense to use in a given situation.

Obviously, if time permits, students may want to collect data on their own class to make comparisons between the class and Wadlow or the trees.

Have students work in pairs on the problem.

Explore 1.3

Suggested Questions If students are struggling, ask questions such as the following:

- *About how many of you would it take to match the height of the giant sequoia?* (For an average student height of 5 ft, it would take 55 students.)

- *What did you do to figure out how to answer that question?* ($275 \div 5$)

- *How does your answer give you ideas about how to think about the questions asked?* (This means that the ratio of the sequoia to the average student is 55 to 1.)

- *If you stand up with your arms extended and turn slowly around, the circle you make is like a tree's spread. About how wide is your arm span?* (About 5 feet.)

- *How do you compare to one of the trees?* (My spread is greater than that of a Florida crossopetulum by a ratio of 5 to 3.)

Going Further
If students finish early, ask:

- *Do you think the trees in the table have similar shapes? Why or why not?* (They are not all similar because their heights and spreads do not have the same ratio. For example, 11 to 3 is not the same as 105 to 216.)

Summarize 1.3

Go over each of the problems. Collect on an overhead or chart paper all of the statements of comparison that students make. Then have the class group them according to the kind of comparison made. Does the statement of comparison use percents, ratios, etc.?

Record the final groups the class puts together and label each group so that they are available for reference in talking about Question D.

Check for Understanding

- *What would the spread of a swamp chestnut have to be for the tree to be similar to a Florida crossopetalum? Explain your reasoning.* (The scale factor of their height is $105 \div 11 \approx 9.54$. The spread should also have the scale factor 9.54. Therefore, I multiply 9.54 by 3 to get the spread for the taller tree. This is 28.62 feet. Alternatively, a student might reason that the swamp chestnut is about 10 times as tall, so the spread should be about 30 feet. Either is a good answer and shows understanding that multiplicative reasoning is required to make a good comparison.)

Mathematical Goal

• Analyze and create comparison statements from given data

Launch

Ask if any of your students know any world records or facts about record holders. Consider asking:

- *What are some different ways that quantities can be written?*
- *What different forms have we seen so far to express the same comparison?*
- *How is a ratio different from a percent and from a fraction?*
- *How can you express something written as a ratio as a fraction?*
- *Does it always make sense to add the two numbers in a situation to get a whole?*
- *What additional statements can you make to compare the giant sequoia to the Florida crossopetalum?*

Have students work in pairs on the problem.

Materials
• Transparency 1.3

Explore

If students are struggling ask questions such as:

- *About how many of you would it take to match the height of the giant sequoia?*
- *What did you do to figure out how to answer that question?*
- *Does your answer give you any ideas about how to think about the questions asked?*
- *If you stand up with your arms extended and turn slowly around, the circle you make is like a tree's spread. About how wide is your arm span?*
- *How do you compare to one of the trees?*

Going Further

- *Do you think these trees have similar shapes? Why or why not?*

Summarize

Go over each of the problems.

Collect on an overhead or chart paper all of the statements of comparison that students make. Then have the class group them according to the kind of comparison made.

Record the final groups the class puts together and label each group so that they are available for reference in talking about Question D.

Materials
• Blank transparencies and transparency markers or chart paper and markers
• Student notebooks

continued on next page

Check for Understanding

• *What would the spread of a swamp chestnut have to be for the tree to be similar to a Florida crossopetulum? Explain your reasoning.*

ACE Assignment Guide for Problem 1.3

Differentiated Instruction
Solutions for All Learners

Core 9, 10
Other *Applications* 8; *Extensions* 36–41; unassigned choices from previous problems

Adapted For suggestions about adapting ACE exercises, see the CMP *Special Needs Handbook.*

Answers to Problem 1.3

A. **1.** It would take about 1.5 coast redwoods since $1.5 \times 80 = 120$.

   2. Yes. ($119 : 80 \approx 120 : 80$, and $120 : 80 = 3 : 2$.)

   3. Yes. ($321 - 275 = 46$.)

   4. About 2 are needed since $107 \times 2 = 214$.

   5. Yes. ($216 \times 50\% = 108$. $107 < 108$.)

   6. Yes. ($31.8 \times 0.75 = 23.85 \approx 23$.)

B. Examples:

   The white oak is less than 11 times as tall as Wadlow.

   The difference between the height of the Florida crossopetalum and the height of Wadlow is about 2 feet.

   Wadlow is about $\frac{1}{12}$ the height of the swamp chestnut oak.

   The height of Wadlow is about (less than) 3% of the height of the coast redwood.

   If the height of the swamp chestnut oak was reduced by a scale factor of $\frac{1}{12}$, its height would be about equal to Wadlow's.

C. Examples:

   The average waist of the men is greater than the circumference of the Florida crossopetalum by a ratio of 20 to 3 ($20 : 3$).

   The average height of the men is $\frac{1}{16}$ the height of the largest white oak.

   The difference between the average arm span of the men and the largest coast redwood spread is 887 in.
   (960 in. $- 73$ in. $= 887$ in.)

   The average height of the men is more than 50% the height of the largest Florida crossopetalum.

D. Difference is used when you want to know "how much more" between two quantities, such as how much taller one person is than another. Ratio is used when you want to compare two quantities and give the scale between them, such as the ratio of males to females in math class. Or, you can use a ratio when you want to know how many times more of one thing there is than another. For example, there are twice as many females as males in math class. In general a fraction is used when you want to give a part-to-whole relationship, such as 10 out of 16 ($\frac{10}{16}$) of the students in class were male. Percent is used when you want to create a common scale to compare two or more sets of data. Percent lets you express something out of 100.

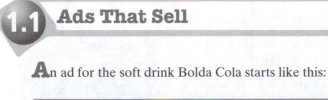

Making Comparisons

Surveys may report people's preferences in food, cars, or political candidates. Often, the favorites are easy to recognize. Explaining how much more popular one choice is than another can be more difficult. In this investigation, you will explore strategies for comparing numbers in accurate and useful ways. As you work on the problems, notice how the different ways of making comparisons send different messages about the numbers being compared.

1.1 Ads That Sell

An ad for the soft drink Bolda Cola starts like this:

To complete the ad, the Bolda Cola company plans to report the results of taste tests. A copywriter for the ad department has proposed four possible conclusions.

Investigation 1 Making Comparisons   **5**

Notes _____

_____

_____

_____

1. In a taste test, people who preferred Bolda Cola outnumbered those who preferred Cola Nola by a ratio of 17,139 to 11,426.

2. In a taste test, 5,713 more people preferred Bolda Cola.

3. In a taste test, 60% of the people preferred Bolda Cola.

4. In a taste test, people who preferred Bolda Cola outnumbered those who preferred Cola Nola by a ratio of 3 to 2.

Problem 1.1 Exploring Ratios and Rates

A. Describe what you think each statement above means.

B. Which of the proposed statements do you think would be most effective in advertising Bolda Cola? Why?

C. Is it possible that all four statements are based on the same survey data? Explain your reasoning.

D. In what other ways can you express the claims in the four proposed advertising statements? Explain.

E. If you were to survey 1,000 cola drinkers, what numbers of Bolda Cola and Cola Nola drinkers would you expect? Explain.

ACE Homework starts on page 10.

1.2 Targeting an Audience

Some middle and high school students earn money by delivering papers, mowing lawns, or baby-sitting. Students with money to spend are a target audience for some radio and television ads. Companies gather information about how much students watch television or listen to the radio. This information influences how they spend their advertising dollars.

6 Comparing and Scaling

Notes _____

_____

_____

_____

As you work on this problem and the rest of the unit, you will see statements about ratio comparisons. In mathematics, it is acceptable to write ratios in different ways. Each way is useful.

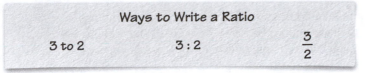

Ways to Write a Ratio

3 to 2   3 : 2 $\frac{3}{2}$

It can be confusing to see a fraction representing a ratio. A ratio is usually, but not always, a *part-to-part* comparison. A fraction usually means a *part-to-whole* comparison. The context can help you decide whether a fraction represents a ratio.

Problem 1.2 Analyzing Comparison Statements

Students at Neilson Middle School are asked if they prefer watching television or listening to the radio. Of 150 students, 100 prefer television and 50 prefer radio.

A. How would you compare student preferences for radio or television?

B. Decide if each statement accurately reports results of the Neilson Middle School survey.

   1. At Neilson Middle School, $\frac{1}{3}$ of the students prefer radio to television.

   2. Students prefer television to radio by a ratio of 2 to 1.

   3. The ratio of students who prefer radio to television is 1 to 2.

   4. The number of students who prefer television is 50 more than the number of students who prefer radio.

   5. The number of students who prefer television is two times the number who prefer radio.

   6. 50% of the students prefer radio to television.

C. Compare statements in parts (4) and (5) above. Which is more informative? Explain.

D. Consider only the accurate statements in Question B.

   1. Which statement would best convince merchants to place ads on radio? Why?

   2. Which statement would best convince merchants to place ads on television? Why?

ACE Homework starts on page 10.

Notes _____

_____

_____

_____

1.3 American Records

People are amazed and amused by records like the highest mountain, the longest fingernails, or the most spoons balanced on a face. What you have learned so far can help you make comparisons. In Problem 1.3, you will compare the largest living trees of different species.

Did You Know?

The champion white "Wye" oak tree near Wye Mills, Maryland, was about 460 years old when it fell during a thunderstorm in 2002. When the tree fell, thousands came by to gawk, shed tears, and pick up a leaf or a twig. Maryland officials carefully gathered and stored as much of the tree as they could until a suitable use could be found.

The challenge to find a white oak bigger than the Wye Mills tree launched the National Register of Big Trees. The search led to the discovery of a new national champion white oak in Virginia.

Go Online
PHSchool.com **For:** Information about big trees
Web Code: ane-9031

You can describe the size of a tree by comparing it to other trees or familiar things.

Selected Champion Trees

Tree Type	Circumference (ft)	Height (ft)	Spread/Diameter (ft)
Giant Sequoia (Calif.)	83.2	275	107
Coast Redwood (Calif.)	79.2	321	80
Swamp Chestnut Oak (Tenn.)	23.0	105	216
Florida Crossopetalum (Fla.)	0.4	11	3
White Oak (Md.)	31.8	96	119

SOURCE: *Washington Post*

8 Comparing and Scaling

STUDENT PAGE

Notes
_____
_____
_____
_____

Problem 1.3 Writing Comparison Statements

A. Use the table on the previous page.

   1. How many coast redwood spreads does it take to equal the spread of the white oak?

   2. Kenning says that the spread of the white oak is greater than that of the coast redwood by a ratio of about 3 to 2. Is he correct? Explain.

   3. Mary says the difference between the heights of the coast redwood and the giant sequoia is 46 feet. Is she correct? Explain.

   4. How many giant sequoia spreads does it take to equal the spread of the swamp chestnut oak?

   5. Jaime says the spread of the giant sequoia is less than 50% of the spread of the swamp chestnut oak. Is he correct?

   6. Len says the circumference of the swamp chestnut oak is about three fourths the circumference of the white oak. Is he correct?

B. The tallest person in history, according to the *Guinness Book of World Records*, was Robert Wadlow. He was nearly 9 feet tall. Write two statements comparing Wadlow to the trees in the table. Use fractions, ratios, percents, or differences.

C. Average waist, height, and arm-span measurements for a small group of adult men are given.

   Waist = 32 inches   Height = 72 inches   Arm Span = 73 inches

   Write two statements comparing the data on these men to the trees in the table. Use fractions, ratios, percents, or differences.

D. When a problem requires comparison of counts or measurements, how do you decide whether to use differences, ratios, fractions, or percents?

ACE Homework starts on page 10.

Investigation 1 Making Comparisons   9

Notes _____

_____

_____

_____

Applications

1. In a comparison taste test of two drinks, 780 students preferred Berry Blast. Only 220 students preferred Melon Splash. Complete each statement.

   a. There were ■ more people who preferred Berry Blast.

   b. In the taste test, ■% of the people preferred Berry Blast.

   c. People who preferred Berry Blast outnumbered those who preferred Melon Splash by a ratio of ■ to ■.

2. In a comparison taste test of new ice creams invented at Moo University, 750 freshmen preferred Cranberry Bog ice cream while 1,250 freshmen preferred Coconut Orange ice cream.

   Complete each statement.

   a. The fraction of freshmen who preferred Cranberry Bog is ■.

   b. The percent of freshmen who preferred Coconut Orange is ■%.

   c. Freshmen who preferred Coconut Orange outnumbered those who preferred Cranberry Bog by a ratio of ■ to ■.

3. A town considers whether to put in curbs along the streets. The ratio of people who support putting in curbs to those who oppose it is 2 to 5.

   a. What fraction of the people *oppose* putting in curbs?

   b. If 210 people in the town are surveyed, how many do you expect to *favor* putting in curbs?

   c. What percent of the people oppose putting in curbs?

10   Comparing and Scaling

Notes _____

_____

_____

_____

Students at a middle school are asked to record how they spend their time from midnight on Friday to midnight on Sunday. Carlos records his data in the table below. Use the table for Exercises 4–7.

Weekend Activities

Activity	Number of Hours
Sleeping	18
Eating	2.5
Recreation	8
Talking on the Phone	2
Watching Television	6
Doing Chores or Homework	2
Other	9.5

4. How would you compare how Carlos spent his time on various activities over the weekend? Explain.

5. Decide if each statement is an accurate description of how Carlos spent his time that weekend.

a. He spent one sixth of his time watching television.

b. The ratio of hours spent watching television to hours spent doing chores or homework is 3 to 1.

c. Recreation, talking on the phone, and watching television took about 33% of his time.

d. Time spent doing chores or homework was only 20% of the time spent watching television.

e. Sleeping, eating, and "other" activities took up 12 hours more than all other activities combined.

6. Estimate what the numbers of hours would be in *your* weekend activity table. Then write a ratio statement like statement (b) to fit your data.

7. Write other accurate statements comparing Carlos's use of weekend time for various activities. Use each concept at least once.

a. ratio

b. difference

c. fraction

d. percent

Investigation 1 Making Comparisons **11**

Notes

8. A class at Middlebury Middle School collected data on the kinds of movies students prefer. Complete each statement using the table.

Types of Movies Preferred by Middlebury Students

Type of Movie	Seventh-Graders	Eighth-Graders
Action	75	90
Comedy	105	150
Total	180	240

a. The ratio of seventh-graders who prefer comedies to eighth-graders who prefer comedies is ■ to ■.

b. The fraction of total students (both seventh- and eighth-graders) who prefer action movies is ■.

c. The fraction of seventh-graders who prefer action movies is ■.

d. The percent of total students who prefer comedies is ■.

e. The percent of eighth-graders who prefer action movies is ■.

f. Grade ■ has the greater percent of students who prefer action movies.

Homework
Help Online
━━ PHSchool.com
For: Help with Exercise 8
Web Code: ane-3108

9. Use the table.

Selected Champion Trees

Tree Type	Height (ft)	Spread (ft)
Florida Crossopetalum	11	3
White Oak	96	119

a. The height of the crossopetalum (kroh soh PET uh lum) is what fraction of the height of the white oak?

b. The height of the crossopetalum is what percent of the height of the white oak?

c. The spread of the crossopetalum is what fraction of the spread of the white oak?

d. The spread of the crossopetalum is what percent of the spread of the white oak?

10. In a survey, 100 students were asked if they prefer watching television or listening to the radio. The results show that 60 students prefer watching television while 40 prefer listening to the radio. Use each concept at least once to express student preferences.

a. ratio
b. percent
c. fraction
d. difference

12 Comparing and Scaling

STUDENT PAGE

Notes _____

_____

_____

_____

(12) 26

STUDENT PAGE

Connections

11. A fruit bar is 5 inches long. The bar will be split into two pieces. For each situation, find the lengths of the two pieces.

   a. One piece is $\frac{3}{10}$ of the whole bar.

   b. One piece is 60% of the bar.

   c. One piece is 1 inch longer than the other.

12. Exercise 11 includes several numbers or quantities: 5 inches, 3, 10, 60%, and 1 inch. Determine whether each number or quantity refers to the whole, a part, or the difference between two parts.

The sketches below show two members of the Grump family. The figures are geometrically similar. Use the figures for Exercises 13–16.

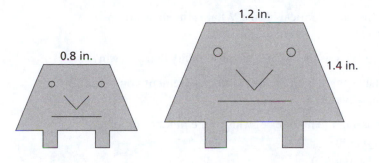

13. Write statements comparing the lengths of corresponding segments in the two Grump drawings. Use each concept at least once.

   a. ratio   **b.** fraction

   c. percent   **d.** scale factor

14. Write statements comparing the areas of the two Grump drawings. Use each concept at least once.

   a. ratio   **b.** fraction

   c. percent   **d.** scale factor

15. How long is the segment in the smaller Grump that corresponds to the 1.4-inch segment in the larger Grump?

16. Multiple Choice The mouth of the smaller Grump is 0.6 inches wide. How wide is the mouth of the larger Grump?

   A. 0.4 in.   **B.** 0.9 in.   **C.** 1 in.   **D.** 1.2 in.

Notes _____

_____

_____

_____

The drawing below shows the Big Wheel spinner used in a game at the Waverly School Fun Night. It costs 20 cents to spin the wheel, and winners receive $1.00. The chart shows the data from 236 spins of the Big Wheel. Use the spinner and the chart for Exercises 17–21.

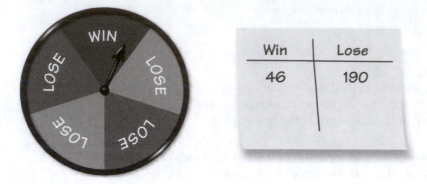

Win	Lose
46	190

17. The sectors of the spinner are identical in size. What is the measure in degrees of each central angle?

18. You play the game once. What is the theoretical probability that you win?

19. Do the results in the table agree with the probability statement you made in Exercise 18? Why or why not?

20. Write statements comparing the number of wins to the number of losses. Use each concept at least once.

    a. ratio   **b.** percent   **c.** difference

21. Which comparison from Exercise 20 is the best way to convey probability information about this game? Explain.

22. Copy the number line below. Add labels for 0.25, $\frac{6}{8}$, $1\frac{3}{4}$, and 1.3.

23. Write two unequal fractions with different denominators. Which fraction is greater? Explain.

24. Write a fraction and a decimal so that the fraction is greater than the decimal. Explain.

Notes _____

_____

_____

_____

Copy each pair of numbers in Exercises 25–33. Insert <, >, or = to make a true statement.

25. $\frac{4}{5}$ ■ $\frac{11}{12}$ **26.** $\frac{14}{21}$ ■ $\frac{10}{15}$ **27.** $\frac{7}{9}$ ■ $\frac{3}{4}$

28. 2.5 ■ 0.259   **29.** 30.17 ■ 30.018   **30.** 0.006 ■ 0.0060

31. 0.45 ■ $\frac{9}{20}$ **32.** $1\frac{3}{4}$ ■ 1.5   **33.** $\frac{1}{4}$ ■ 1.3

Extensions

34. Rewrite this ad so that it will be more effective.

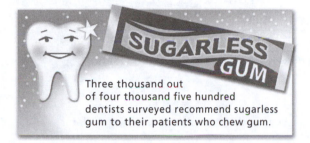

Three thousand out of four thousand five hundred dentists surveyed recommend sugarless gum to their patients who chew gum.

35. Use the table below.

Money Spent for Food

Where Food Is Eaten	1990	1998
Home	$303,900,000,000	$401,800,000,000
Away From Home	$168,800,000,000	$354,400,000,000

SOURCE: U.S. Census Bureau. Go to PHSchool.com for a data update. Web Code: ang-9041

a. Compare money spent on food eaten at home and food eaten away from home to the total money spent for food. Write statements for each year.

b. Explain how the statements you wrote in part (a) show the money spent for food away from home increasing or decreasing in relation to the total spent for food.

Notes _____

_____

_____

_____

Advertising Spending in the United States (millions)		
Placement	1990	2000
Newspapers	$32,281	$46,582
Magazines	$6,803	$11,096
Television	$29,073	$50,843
Radio	$8,726	$16,930
Yellow Pages	$8,926	$12,666
Internet	$0	$1,840
Direct Mail	$23,370	$41,601
Other	$20,411	$33,671
Total	$129,590	$215,229

SOURCE: U.S. Census Bureau. Go to **PHSchool.com** for a data update. Web code: ang–9041

36. Which placement has the greatest difference in advertising dollars between 1990 and 2000?

37. Find the percent of all advertising dollars spent on each placement in 1990.

38. Find the percent of all advertising dollars spent on each placement in 2000.

39. Use your results from Exercises 36–38. Write several sentences describing how advertising spending changed from 1990 to 2000.

40. Suppose you were thinking about investing in either a television station or a radio station. Which method of comparing advertising costs (differences or percents) makes television seem like the better investment? Which makes radio seem like the better investment?

41. Suppose you are a reporter writing an article about trends in advertising over time. Which method of comparison would you choose?

Notes _____

_____

_____

_____

Mathematical Reflections 1

In this investigation, you explored several ways of comparing numbers. The problems were designed to help you understand and use different comparison strategies and recognize when each is most useful. The following questions will help you summarize what you have learned.

Think about your answers to these questions. Discuss your ideas with other students and your teacher. Then write a summary of your findings in your notebook.

1. Explain what you think each word means when it is used to make a comparison.

   a. ratio

   b. percent

   c. fraction

   d. difference

2. Give an example of a situation using each concept to compare two quantities.

   a. ratio

   b. percent

   c. fraction

   d. difference

Investigation 1 Making Comparisons **17**

Notes _____

_____

_____

_____

Investigation 1

ACE Assignment Choices

Differentiated Instruction
Solutions for All Learners

Problem 1.1
Core 1, 2, 34
Other *Applications* 3, *Connections* 11–16

Problem 1.2
Core 4, 5, 7
Other *Applications* 6, *Connections* 17–33, *Extensions* 35; unassigned choices from previous problems

Problem 1.3
Core 9, 10
Other *Applications* 8, *Extensions* 36–41; unassigned choices from previous problems

Adapted For suggestions about adapting Exercise 1 and other ACE exercises, see the CMP *Special Needs Handbook.*
Connecting to Prior Units 11, 12: *Bits and Pieces I, Bits and Pieces II*; 13–16: *Stretching and Shrinking*; 17–21: *Shapes and Designs, How Likely Is It?*; 22–33: *Bits and Pieces I*

Applications

1. **a.** 560
   b. 78%
   c. 39 to 11 (or 780 to 220, 195 to 55)

2. **a.** $\frac{750}{2,000} = \frac{3}{8}$
   b. 62.5; here students need to recognize that the fraction they need is $\frac{5}{8}$, and $5 \div 8 = 0.625$.
   c. 5 to 3

3. **a.** $\frac{5}{7}$
   b. 60
   c. About 71% (71.429%)

4. Possible answer: Fractions are a logical way to compare how students spent their time as they compare the time devoted to each activity (part) to the whole time investigated (whole).

5. **a.** No, $\frac{6}{48} = \frac{1}{8}$.
   b. Yes, 6 : 2 = 3 : 1.
   c. Yes, 8 + 2 + 6 = 16.
      16 ÷ 48 ≈ 0.3333 ≈ 33%.
   d. No, $\frac{2}{6}$ ≈ 0.3333, 0.3333 ≈ 33% ≠ 20%.
   e. Yes, 18 + 2.5 + 9.5 = 30; 48 − 30 = 18; 30 − 18 = 12.

6. Answers may vary.

7. Possible answers:
   a. The ratio of hours Carlos spent sleeping to hours he spent watching television is 3 to 1. The ratio of hours spent on the phone to doing chores or homework is 1 to 1.
   b. The difference between the number of hours Carlos spent sleeping and the number he spent watching television is 12.
   c. Carlos spent $\frac{1}{6}$ of his time on recreation.
   d. Carlos spent 50% of his time watching television and sleeping. Carlos spent about 33% of his time on recreation, watching television, and doing chores and homework.

8. **a.** 7 to 10
   b. $\frac{75 + 90}{180 + 240} = \frac{11}{28}$
   c. $\frac{75}{180} = \frac{5}{12}$
   d. $\frac{17}{28}$ ≈ 0.6071, which is about 61%.
   e. $\frac{90}{240}$ = 0.375 or 37.5%
   f. Grade 7. Grade 7 is 41.7% and Grade 8 is 37.5%.

9. a. $\frac{11}{96}$ ($\approx \frac{1}{9}$) b. About 11.5% (11.458%)

c. $\frac{3}{119}$ ($\approx \frac{1}{40}$) d. About 2.5% (2.521%)

10. Possible answers:

a. Students prefer radio to television by a ratio of 2 to 3 (2 : 3). Students prefer television to radio by a ratio of 3 to 2 (3 : 2).

b. 60% of students prefer television and 40% of students prefer radio.

c. $\frac{3}{5}$ of students prefer television to radio.

d. The difference between the number of students who prefer television to radio is 20.

Connections

11. a. One piece will be 1.5 in. and the other will be 3.5 in. A ratio of 3 : 7 also means that one piece will be 0.3 of the fruit bar and the other piece will be 0.7 of the fruit bar. Thus, 0.3 × 5 = 1.5 and 0.7 × 5 = 3.5.

b. One piece will be 3 in. long and the other will be 2 in. long (60% = 0.6, 0.6 × 5 = 3).

c. One piece will be 3 in. long and the other will be 2 in. long.

12. The 3 in the numerator in part (a) and the 60% in part (b) each represent a part; the 5 inches in the problem text and the 10 in the denominator in part (a) represent a whole; and 1 inch in part (c) represents the difference between parts.

For the Teacher Discuss what techniques were used by students to arrive at each of the answers. Which part was easiest to answer? Which way of phrasing the question (in terms of fractions, ratios, percents, difference) made the most sense for solving these problems?

13. a. The ratio of the lengths of the top sides of the two Grumps is 0.8 to 1.2 or 2 to 3.

b. Since they are similar, any side of the small Grump is $\frac{2}{3}$ the length of the larger Grump.

c. The top side of the small Grump is about 67% of the length of the top side of the larger Grump.

d. The scale factor from the small Grump to the large Grump is 1.5.

14. a. The ratio of the areas of the two Grumps is 4 to 9.

b. The area of the smaller Grump is $\frac{4}{9}$ the area of the larger Grump.

c. The area of the smaller Grump is about 44% the area of the larger Grump.

d. The area scale factor from the small Grump to the large Grump is 2.25.

15. 0.93 in. (The scale factor is 1.5. Therefore, 1.4 ÷ 1.5 ≈ 0.93.)

16. B (0.6 times the scale factor of 1.5 equals 0.9.)

17. 72°

18. 1 out of 5 times, or 20%

19. Agree, because 46 ÷ (46 + 190) ≈ 0.195 = 19.5%.

20. a. The ratio of wins to losses is 46 to 190, which is about 1 to 4, or 1 : 4.

b. One wins about 20% of the time and loses about 80% of the time.

c. The difference between the number of losses and wins is 144 (144 more people lost than won).

21. Percents are an easy way to convey the probability of winning. Fractions also convey the understanding easily. In both instances, you can express the chance of either winning or losing out of all the times the game was played.

22.

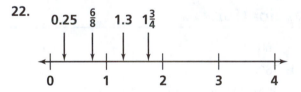

For the Teacher Discuss how students are representing the numbers to place on the number line. Are they changing the way they are represented in the problem to a consistent means, such as all fractions or all decimals, etc.? What seems to be a natural way to begin dividing the segments on the number line?

23. Possible answer: $\frac{3}{4} > \frac{2}{3}$; $\frac{3}{4}$ is greater because it is closer to 1. Its decimal equivalent is 0.75 as compared to about 0.67, the decimal approximation of $\frac{2}{3}$.

24. Possible answer: $\frac{1}{2} > 0.25$ ($0.5 > 0.25$)

25. $< (0.8 < 0.91,$ or $\frac{48}{60} < \frac{55}{60})$

26. $= (\frac{2}{3} = \frac{2}{3})$

27. $> (0.78 > 0.75,$ or $\frac{28}{36} > \frac{27}{36})$

28. $>$ (2.5 is greater than 1, and 0.259 is less than 1.)

29. $>$ (Because 30 is the same in both, compare the tenths place; $1 > 0$, so $30.17 > 30.018$.)

30. $=$ (Because the first three decimal places are the same in both, compare the next decimal place. The unwritten 0 in 0.006 equals the 0 in 0.0060, so $0.006 = 0.0060$.)

31. $= (0.45 = 0.45,$ or $\frac{9}{20} = \frac{9}{20})$

32. $> (\frac{7}{4} > \frac{6}{4},$ or $1.75 > 1.5)$

33. $< (\frac{1}{4}$ is less than 1, and 1.3 is greater than 1)

Extensions

34. Possible answer: About 67% of dentists recommend sugarless gum to their patients who chew gum. 2 out of 3 dentists recommend sugarless gum to their patients who chew gum.

35. a. In 1990, about 64% of money spent on food was spent on food eaten at home. 36% was spent on food eaten away from home. (The total amount of money spent on food in 1990 was $472,700,000,000). In 1998, about 53% of money spent on food was for food eaten at home. 47% was spent on food eaten away from home.

b. The amount of money spent on food eaten away from home is increasing in relation to the total amount spent on food. 47% was spent on food eaten away from home in 1998 as compared to 36% in 1990.

36. television

37–38. (Figure 1)

39. Possible answers:

Overall, the percent spent on advertising for each medium remains relatively consistent over the 10-year span from 1990 to 2000.

The percent spent on magazine advertising did not change over the 10 years.

The greatest difference in spending over the 10 years was in television.

The least difference in spending over the 10 years was in the Internet.

The greatest percent change in spending was in newspapers, down to 22% from 25%.

Figure 1

Advertising Spending in the United States (millions)

Placement	Difference in Spending Between 1990 and 2000	Percent of Advertising Spending in 1990	Percent of Advertising Spending in 2000
Newspapers	$14,301	24.9 (25)	21.6 (22)
Magazines	$4,293	5.25 (5)	5.2 (5)
Television	$21,770	22.4 (22)	23.6 (24)
Radio	$8,204	6.7 (7)	7.9 (8)
Yellow Pages	$3,740	6.9 (7)	5.9 (6)
Internet	$1,840	0	0.86 (1)
Direct Mail	$18,231	18.0 (18)	19.3 (19)
Other	$13,260	15.8 (16)	15.6 (16)
Total	$85,639		

40. For television, discussing the difference makes television seem like a better investment because the percent of expenditures remained relatively consistent (22% as compared to 24%), yet the difference in actual dollar amount was 21,770,000,000. The difference in actual dollar amounts is therefore more impressive. The same is also true for radio as the difference between dollar expenditures would be impressive at 8,204,000,000 as opposed to the change in percents, from 7% in 1990 to 8% in 2000.

41. Percents are easily understood and often used to discuss trends over time. In this case, they would indicate the relative consistency of expenditures per medium. The differences would highlight the impressive overall dollar increase in advertising. The differences would also make a better headline. However, the trends in advertising would be more accurately represented by using percents.

For the Teacher Discuss how such big differences can exist in terms of actual expenditures while percents can remain relatively unchanged.

Possible Answers to Mathematical Reflections

1. **a.** A ratio can compare two parts of a whole. *The ratio of girls to boys is 5 to 4* means that for every 5 girls there are 4 boys. If there were 20 girls, there would be 16 boys. In this case, the parts of the whole are the number of girls in the group (5) to the number of boys in the group (4).

   b. Percents quantify amounts in terms of "out of 100." *Girls comprise 56% of the class* means that if there were 100 students, 56 would be girls.

   c. Fractions illustrate the amount of a part to the whole. *Four ninths of the class members are boys* means that if there were 9 students total, 4 would be boys. Another way to look at it is that for every 9 class members, 4 of them are boys. Therefore, if there are 18 class members, 8 would be boys.

   d. Difference is used when you want to know "how much more" between two quantities, such as how much taller one person is than another.

2. Possible answers:

   a. Ratio—Comparing the number of seventh-graders to eighth-graders on a middle school track team.

   b. Percent—Comparing preferences for regular soda versus diet soda.

   c. Fraction—Comparing the portion of red Skittles in two different bags out of all the Skittles in each bag.

   d. Difference—Comparing the distance between two cities or comparing the weight of two animals.

   For the Teacher You might want to discuss when it is appropriate to change a ratio into a fraction or a fraction into a percent.

Mathematical and Problem-Solving Goals

- Become comfortable with ratio and related forms of comparisons to solve problems
- Find equivalent ratios
- Further develop strategies for comparing ratios

Summary of Problems

Problem 2.1 Mixing Juice

Students look at the part-to-whole relationship in a recipe for juice and use fractions, decimals, or percents derived from fractions to make comparisons. Students informally explore rates and ratios, using proportional reasoning to determine how to combine orange juice concentrate and water to make enough orange juice for a given number of people.

Problem 2.2 Sharing Pizza

Students compare two table sizes and two amounts of pizza. They are challenged to determine whether the two arrangements allocate pizza to people in a fair way.

Problem 2.3 Finding Equivalent Ratios

In this problem, students more systematically explore scaling ratios up and down to help answer questions or solve problems. Students create a table to keep track of different kinds of mixes and look for patterns in the table.

INVESTIGATION 2

	Suggested Pacing	Materials for Students	Materials for Teachers	ACE Assignments
All	$4\frac{1}{2}$ days	Calculators, blank transparencies and transparency markers or chart paper and markers (optional), student notebooks	Transparency markers	
2.1	1 day			1–3, 9–13
2.2	1 day		Transparency 2.2	4, 5, 14–18, 22
2.3	2 days		Transparencies 2.3A and 2.3B	6–8, 19–21, 23, 24
MR	$\frac{1}{2}$ day			

Goal

- Become comfortable with ratio and related forms of comparisons to solve problems

Students encounter an open-ended situation in which comparison is needed to make a decision. In this problem, students are challenged to compare drink recipes. They use proportional reasoning to figure out how to make different mixes of orange juice for 240 people.

The first page of Investigation 2 in the Student Edition has a Did You Know? that contains four statements of quantitative comparison. These statements show ratios, percents, and fraction statements being used to give information about situations. This helps to focus the students' attention on ratio comparisons and the ways that such comparisons are represented.

You need to make a decision about whether you think your students need this introduction before or after they have had time to work on Problem 2.1. There is an advantage to posing the problem in an open way, allowing the students to find many different ways to think about the situation. A discussion about ratios after the students have their own ideas about the problem is effective. Revisiting the problem with an eye on ratios can be done in the summary.

Launch 2.1

Launch Problem 2.1 by making sure that students understand the context.

Suggested Questions

- *How many students have made orange juice from a can before?*

- *What was involved in making it?*

You may want to bring in a can of frozen orange juice (thawed) and, with your class, actually make juice, following the instructions on the can. You can discuss the fact that you have one container of concentrated juice and to this you add three containers of water (or whatever it says on the container of concentrate). Point out that the recipes given in the problem are different from the one on the can. At camp, the frozen concentrate comes in a very large container without mixing proportions given.

This is a challenging problem for students. Some teachers do a launch and then pull the class back together to discuss their initial thinking about the different recipes. This gives a chance for groups to hear different strategies. Together, Questions A and B of the problem can be discussed, and then the groups can be challenged to solve Questions C and D of the problem.

Have students work together in groups of three to four students.

Explore 2.1

As students are working on Questions A and B, circulate asking questions. If a group has a conjecture about most and least orangey, ask them to explain why. Some students will use naive strategies such as simply finding the difference between the number of cans of concentrate and ignore the water.

Suggested Questions Ask questions to challenge students' ideas.

- *Can I keep adding cans of water without making the juice less orangey?*

Other students will propose that $\frac{2}{3}$ of the juice in Mix A is concentrate. Ask:

- *How much juice is made from one recipe?*

Leave the students to sort out what the actual fraction of the juice in each recipe is concentrate. Usually the students will begin to question their initial thoughts and recognize that the whole in Mix A is 5 cups so the fraction that is concentrate is $\frac{2}{5}$.

Question C is designed to raise the issue of writing comparison statements using fractions from data such as this. The questions suggested above are appropriate here as well.

For Question D, if students are stuck on the question of making a recipe to feed 240, ask them to consider Mix A. Have them review how much total liquid (concentrate and water) is in this batch (5 cups).

Suggested Questions Use these questions as guides.

- *What are your ideas about how many people one batch of this juice might serve?*

- *What if each serving is an 8 oz. glass, the same as 1 cup?* (5 servings are possible)

- *What if each serving is $\frac{1}{2}$ cup?* (10 servings are possible)

- *If you were going to serve juice to 50 people, how many batches would you have to make if each person gets $\frac{1}{2}$ cup of juice?* (5 batches)

- *What are different strategies you might use to answer this question?* (Students might just divide 50 people by the 10 servings per batch to determine that 5 batches are needed. Alternatively, some students may reason that if 1 batch makes 10 servings, then 2 batches make 20 servings, 3 batches make 30 servings, 4 batches make 40 servings, and 5 batches make 50 servings. Students may choose to make a table from which to reason.)

Servings of Juice

Number of Batches	1	2	3	4	5	6	7
Servings	10	20	30	40	50	60	70

You also may want to do some drawings to match this table. Students may want to sketch ten glasses to represent one batch. Then they can repeat these ten glasses for each batch, showing that the number of glasses is a multiple of 10 as the number of batches increases.

Question E asks for another kind of reasoning. Here, rather than making several batches, the students are asked to figure out how to make exactly one cup of juice that fits each of the recipes. In essence they have to partition accurately one whole into two parts—one part that represents the water and the other part that represents the concentrate. If a group is stuck, ask how many parts they will have to partition a cup into to make the cup of juice fit Mix A.

Revisit Questions A and B, then discuss C and D. This summary should be a time for the students to give their ideas and to tell why they think their ideas make sense. You want the students to leave this problem having experienced several problem-solving strategies, including an emphasis on ratios.

Students might have a variety of ways to reason about the questions in this problem. One way to express the relationships of concentrate to *total liquid* in a batch is to write part-to-whole ratios. Then express the ratios as fractions and order the fractions (and thus the ratios) from least to greatest. Using prior knowledge about fractions, students may represent the fractions as decimals so that the comparisons are easy. From this, the students identify which is the most orangey (most concentrate, greatest fraction) and which is the least orangey (least concentrate, least fraction). Be sure that you ask the students to tell you what the fractions mean. The $\frac{1}{3}$ for Mix C means that one cup of juice has $\frac{1}{3}$ of a cup of concentrate and $\frac{2}{3}$ of a cup of water. Using this strategy, the order is from least to most orangey:

Mix C $\frac{1}{3}$ Least Orangey	Mix B $\frac{5}{14}$	Mix D $\frac{3}{8}$	Mix A $\frac{2}{5}$ Most Orangey

Suggested Questions The main point that you want to be sure students think about is:

- *What does it mean to be the most orangey tasting? To be the least orangey tasting?*

You want to help the students see that they need to find a way to make something the same in order to make comparisons. Here are some possibilities that students have developed:

1. Make equal amounts of each mix and compare the amount of water or concentrate needed to make the chosen amount. For example, make 840 cups. Then we have 168 batches of Mix A; 60 batches of Mix B; 280 batches of Mix C; and 105 batches of Mix D. So the concentrate needed is 336 cups for Mix A; 300 cups for Mix B; 280 cups for Mix C; and 315 cups for Mix D. Mix A is most orangey and Mix C is least orangey.

2. Write a part-to-whole fraction from the amount of concentrate in each mix and the total amount of juice a batch of the mix makes. Find common denominators for these fractions to make comparisons. (Note that this is the same as making the same amount of each mix.) The fractions of concentrate would be $\frac{336}{840}$, $\frac{300}{840}$, $\frac{280}{840}$, and $\frac{315}{840}$.

3. Express the part-to-whole ratios as percents and compare. (This is in essence making the same amount of each mix.) The percents are 40%, 35.7%, 33.3%, and 37.5%.

4. Draw pictures showing how much water for each cup of concentrate is in each mix. (This makes the amount of concentrate, the denominator in the part-to-part fraction, the same.) The goal is to partition the water rectangles so that each cup of concentrate gets the same amount of water.

For Mix A, the middle rectangle is split into two equal parts and one part is given to each cup of concentrate.

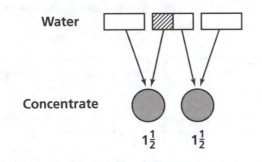

So we have $1\frac{1}{2}$ cups of water for each cup of concentrate.

For Mix B, half the rectangles are split into five parts so that 1 whole and $\frac{4}{5}$ of another can be given to each cup of concentrate.

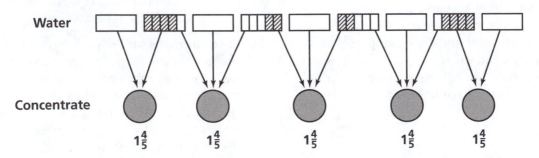

So we have $1\frac{4}{5}$ cups of water for each cup of concentrate.

For Mix C, we give all of the water to the one concentrate and get 2 cups of water for each cup of concentrate.

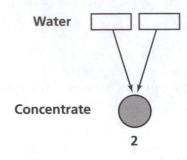

For Mix D, we have to partition two of the water into three parts so that we can share equally by giving 1 whole and $\frac{2}{3}$ of another to each cup of concentrate.

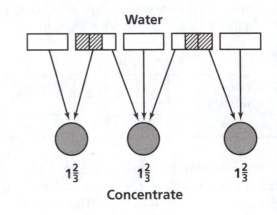

So we have $1\frac{2}{3}$ cups of water for each cup of concentrate.

5. Figure out how much water goes with each cup of concentrate. (This makes the denominators of the ratios the same.) $\frac{1\frac{1}{2}}{1}$, $\frac{1\frac{4}{5}}{1}$, $\frac{2}{1}$; and $\frac{1\frac{2}{3}}{1}$. Notice that this time we focus on the most and least watery. Most watery is $\frac{2}{1}$.

If we figure out how much concentrate goes into each cup of water, we get $\frac{2}{3}$, $\frac{5}{9}$, $\frac{1}{2}$, $\frac{3}{5}$, where $\frac{1}{2}$ represents the least orangey.

6. Make the number of cups of concentrate the same.

A: 30 cups of concentrate to 45 cups of water

B: 30 cups of concentrate to 54 cups of water

C: 30 cups of concentrate to 60 cups of water

D: 30 cups of concentrate to 50 cups of water

Other students might keep the number of cups of water the same and calculate the cups of concentrate.

7. Make a table to show the amounts of concentrate and water for each mix, and continue the values in the tables for multiples of the mixes until you have the same amount of water for each and can make a comparison.

When you hit 90 cups of water for each mix you will have: Mix A: 60 to 90; Mix B: 50 to 90; Mix C: 45 to 90; Mix D: 54 to 90.

Check for Understanding

• *Which of the following will taste most orangey: 2 cups of concentrate and 3 cups of water; 4 cups of concentrate and 6 cups of water; or 10 cups of concentrate and 15 cups of water?* (Research has shown that many students have preconceptions about the recipe scaling reasoning that will lead them to choose the recipe with most concentrate, even though the ratio of concentrate to water is the same in all three!)

Question C

Call on some students to explain their thinking. One example of a student response is:

$\frac{5}{9}$ is a part-to-part comparison and does not tell you what fraction of Mix B is concentrate. $\frac{5}{14}$ is a part-to-whole comparison and does tell you what fraction of the mix is concentrate.

Question D

Again let groups report their results and give reasons why they think their results make sense. Here are four different ways of reasoning that groups have used with the different recipes.

Method 1

Some groups find the number of batches needed to make 120 cups of juice from each mix. Then they multiply to find the total amount of concentrate and the total amount of water. With Mix A, for example, one batch makes 5 cups of juice. We need 120, so we divide 120 by 5 to get the number of batches needed. We need 24 batches. Since we need 2 cups of concentrate for one batch, we need 2×24 cups of concentrate for 24 batches. This gives 48 cups of concentrate. We need 3 cups of water per batch. So we need 3×24 cups of water for 24 batches. This is 72 cups of water. Since the amount of concentrate plus the amount of water equals 120 cups, we have a check on our work.

Method 2

Some groups use a special strategy for Mix C. They picture the 120 cups of water divided into three parts. Each part has 40 cups. We need 1 part concentrate, so this is 40 cups of concentrate. We need 2 parts water, so this is 80 cups of water.

Method 3

Some groups make a rate (ratio) table like the one here to help scale up.

Mix D

Concentrate (cups)	Water (cups)
3	5
6	10
9	15
12	20
15	25
18	30
21	35
24	40
27	45
30	50
33	55
36	60
39	65
42	70
45	75

They recognize that the sum of 45 and 75 is the 120 that they need. This means 45 cups of concentrate and 75 cups of water. This strategy is clearly scaling ratios in the same way that students have found equivalent fractions.

Method 4

Some students use the strategy of finding equivalent fractions for the fraction of concentrate to the whole with 840 as the denominator, and then simplify to equivalent fractions with 120 as the denominator. Of course, Mix B makes 14 cups total, and since 14 is not a factor of 120, we cannot get a whole number of cups of concentrate.

Mix A	Mix B	Mix C	Mix D
$\frac{2}{5}$	$\frac{5}{14}$	$\frac{1}{3}$	$\frac{3}{8}$
$\frac{336}{840}$	$\frac{300}{840}$	$\frac{280}{840}$	$\frac{315}{840}$
$\frac{48}{120}$	$\approx \frac{43}{120}$	$\frac{40}{120}$	$\frac{45}{120}$

Question E

This question is another way to focus students on the difference between part-to-whole and part-to-part comparisons. If you make exactly 1 cup of each mix, then you must deal with part-to-whole.

2.1 Mixing Juice

Mathematical Goal

- Become comfortable with ratio and related forms of comparisons to solve problems

Launch

Consider using the Did You Know? to focus students' attention on ratio comparisons and the ways that such comparisons are represented.

Make sure students understand the context. Ask:

- *How many students have made orange juice from a can before?*
- *What was involved in making it?*

Consider bringing in a can of frozen orange juice (thawed) and actually making juice with your class.

Discuss the differences between the recipe on the juice can and those used in the problem.

Have students work in groups of three to four students.

Explore

Circulate and consider asking the following questions:

- *Can I keep adding cans of water without making the juice less orangey?*
- *How much juice is made from one recipe?*
- *What are your ideas about how many people one batch of this juice might serve?*
- *What if each serving is an 8 oz. glass, the same as 1 cup?*
- *What if each serving is $\frac{1}{2}$ cup?*
- *If you were going to serve juice to 50 people, how many batches would you have to make if each person gets $\frac{1}{2}$ cup of juice?*
- *What are different strategies you might use to answer this question?*

Materials

- Blank transparencies and transparency markers or chart paper and markers (optional)

Summarize

Consider revisiting Questions A, B, C, and D. Have groups report results or share their thinking.

Students might have a variety of ways to reason about the questions in this problem.

You want to help the students see that they need to find a way to make something the same in order to make comparisons.

Materials

- Student notebooks

continued on next page

- Which of the following will taste most orangey: 2 cups of concentrate and 3 cups of water; 4 cups of concentrate and 6 cups of water; or 10 cups of concentrate and 15 cups of water?

ACE Assignment Guide for Problem 2.1

Differentiated Instruction
Solutions for All Learners

Core 1–3, 9, 10
Other *Connections* 11–13

Adapted For suggestions about adapting Exercise 1 and other ACE exercises, see the CMP *Special Needs Handbook*.
Connecting to Prior Units 9–11: *Bits and Pieces I*; 13: *How Likely Is It?*

Answers to Problem 2.1

A. Mix A will make the most orangey juice. (See possible explanations in the Summarize section.)

B. Mix C will make the least orangey juice. (See possible explanations in the Summarize section.)

C. $\frac{5}{14}$ of Mix B is concentrate is correct because a part-to-whole comparison is needed to say the fraction part of the mix that is concentrate.

D. 1. Mix A: Each batch serves 10 people a half cup, so you need 24 batches.

Mix B : Each batch serves 28 people a half cup, so you need about 9 batches.

Mix C: Each batch serves 6 people a half cup, so you need 40 batches.

Mix D: Each batch serves 16 people a half cup, so you need 15 batches.

2. The table below shows how much of each ingredient is needed to serve 240 people. (See possible explanations in the Summarize section.)

	Mix			
	A	**B**	**C**	**D**
Ratio of concentrate to water	2 to 3	5 to 9	1 to 2	3 to 5
Number of batches	24	8.6	40	15
Cups concentrate	48	43	40	45
Cups water	72	77	80	75
Total cups of juice	120	120	120	120

For the entries under Mix B, 43 and 77 are approximations. You might want to ask why you cannot make exactly 120 cups with whole numbers by scaling up this recipe?

E. Mix A would need $\frac{2}{5}$ cup of concentrate and $\frac{3}{5}$ cup of water. Mix B would need $\frac{5}{14}$ cup of concentrate and $\frac{9}{14}$ cup water. Mix C would need $\frac{1}{3}$ cup of concentrate and $\frac{2}{3}$ cup of water. Mix D would need $\frac{3}{8}$ cup of concentrate and $\frac{5}{8}$ cup of water.

Goal

- Continue to work with ratio comparisons

In this problem, the question involves a comparison between two sizes of tables and two amounts of pizza. The question is whether the two situations are fair in terms of amount of pizza per person. The numbers are small, so that the idea of comparison can be the central focus. The problem is also designed to surface any wrong ideas students have about difference as a comparison strategy so that these can be challenged.

Launch 2.2

To get the students engaged in the problem you might describe the situation and look at the two kinds of tables.

Suggested Questions Ask, but do not analyze, whether each idea is a good one:

- *At which table would you choose to sit?*

- *Do others have a different choice?*

Talk together about what the problem is asking students to do so that they will have no problem interpreting the questions.

Stress that each group should prepare to explain their strategy and why they think their strategy for solving the problem is appropriate. Also stress that you are very interested in the explanation of why students think their answers are correct. You should encourage the groups to try to find more than one way to make the comparison.

Partners or groups work well for this problem.

Explore 2.2

By this time, most of your students should find Question A of the problem very easy, although many of them may have difficulty discussing their solutions in the language of ratios. This is an example of a ratio that is related to quantities of different kinds—people and pizzas.

Suggested Questions As you circulate, ask:

- *Can you find another way to think about Question A? Are your two ways related? If so, how?*

Question B helps students to realize what the 3 and the 8 represent in the fraction $\frac{3}{8}$ in terms of pizzas and number of people at a table.

Question C requires students to figure out what another student has done and the claims she makes and then to decide whether her method is correct. Here Selena gets the correct answer for the wrong reasons. The second question is meant to push students to see that computing a difference makes no sense here.

Question D is harder. However, students developed strategies in the orange juice problem that are helpful here. You might need to remind them to review their earlier work.

Look for students with ideas and strategies that should be shared in the summary. Also look for students who are reasoning incorrectly. Discuss their thinking in a way that supports them in sorting out why their thinking is incorrect.

Summarize 2.2

Students will probably come up with a variety of ways of reasoning about this problem. Let them present to and quiz each other on their personally constructed approaches. For example, some students may say that they will join the large table, since it has more pizza, or the small table since it has fewer people to share pizza. In either case, using one number (the number of people or the number of pizzas) does not give enough information about the situation.

Suggested Questions You can point this out by asking questions like these:

- *What if one table had 30 people and 5 pizzas and another had 5 people and 4 pizzas? Would you decide where to sit by choosing the table with the most pizza? Why or why not?*

• *What if one table had 10 people and 5 pizzas and another had 3 people and 1 pizza? Would you decide where to sit by just choosing the one with the fewest people? Why or why not?*

• *Does it make sense to add people and pizzas to make a whole population?* (No.)

There are two numbers associated with each table—the number of pizza and the number of people. Both of these values should be considered when the comparisons are made.

• *What is the ratio of pizza to people at the two tables?* (4 to 10 and 3 to 8)

• *What do these ratios mean?* (pizzas to people)

• *Can you scale these ratios so that they have a number in common?* (Yes. 4 to 10 and 16 to 40 are equivalent ratios; and 3 to 8 and 15 to 40 are equivalent ratios. This would mean 16 pizzas for 40 people compared to 15 pizzas for 40 people. Alternatively, a student might scale to 12 : 30 and 12 : 32.)

• *So, now which table gives you the most pizza?* (The 10-person table with 4 pizzas, which has a ratio equivalent to a 40-person table with 16 pizzas.)

• *Can you scale the ratios so that the number of pizzas is equal to make the comparison easy?* (Yes. 12 pizzas to 30 people is equivalent to the ratio of 4 pizzas for 10 people, and 12 pizzas for 32 people is equivalent to the ratio of 3 pizzas to 8 people. This means that you want to sit at the bigger table!)

Some students who anticipate the next investigation will compute unit rates. This is fine, just be sure ratio arguments are also considered.

The large table has 4 pizzas to share with 10 people; this is $\frac{4}{10}$ pizza per person. At the smaller table, there are 3 pizzas to be shared with 8 people. Each person may have $\frac{3}{8}$ of a pizza.

• *If you want to go to the table with the most pizza per person, at which table do you sit? How do $\frac{4}{10}$ pizza and $\frac{3}{8}$ pizza compare?*

Students may want to look at equivalent fractions, decimals, or percents. If students look at the equivalent fractions, they could use 40 as a common unit so that $\frac{4}{10} = \frac{16}{40}$ and $\frac{3}{8} = \frac{15}{40}$. Because

$\frac{16}{40}$ is greater than $\frac{15}{40}$, a student would get more pizza by sitting at a larger table. Some students will divide to write the fractions as decimals. This is fine. Just ask what labels the decimals should have.

Call on a couple of students to discuss Question B. The intent is to raise questions about difference as a way of making comparisons. Take the time to have the following discussion. You might assign these problems as part of the homework and discuss them the next day.

Let's look at Selena's reasoning in a fraction context: Selena compares fractions by subtracting the numerators and the denominators. She says the fraction with the lesser difference is closer to 1 and thus the greater fraction. Check Selena's method on these fractions to see if it correctly predicts which is greater:

a. $\frac{3}{4}$ and $\frac{3}{5}$ **b.** $\frac{2}{7}$ and $\frac{3}{7}$

c. $\frac{8}{11}$ and $\frac{16}{20}$ **d.** $\frac{8}{11}, \frac{9}{12}, \frac{10}{13}, \frac{11}{14}, \frac{12}{15}$

e. Put the fractions from part (d) in order from least to greatest.

Suggested Questions

• *What happens to a fraction when you add one to both the numerator and the denominator? Is the new fraction greater or lesser?*

Question D of the problem requires finding a ratio equivalent to 8 large tables to 5 small tables that gives seating space for 240 students. Have student groups share their thinking even if they are not able to get a final solution to the problem. Ask groups to tell what they know for sure and why.

The complexity in this problem is that we have two ratios with which to deal. A large table seats 10 people and a small table seats 8 people. One way to think about the problem is to ask what one "group" of tables, 8 large and 5 small would seat. This would seat 80 + 40 people or 120 people. So we need two "groups," which would be 16 large tables and 10 small tables.

Mathematical Goal

- Continue to work with ratio comparisons

Launch

Ask, but do not analyze:

- *At which table would you choose to sit?*
- *Do others have a different choice?*

Talk about the problem.

Have students work in partners or groups.

Materials

- Transparency 2.2
- Transparency markers (optional)

Explore

Have students work on Question A and circulate.

Consider asking:

- *Can you find another way to think about Question A? Are your two ways related? If so, how?*

Look for students with ideas and strategies that should be shared in the summary. Also look for any wrong reasoning that may surface in a way that supports students in sorting out why their thinking is incorrect. Discuss their thinking.

Materials

- Blank transparencies and markers (optional)

Summarize

Pose questions such as:

- *What if one table had 30 people and 5 pizzas and another had 5 people and 4 pizzas? Would you decide where to sit by choosing the table with the most pizza? Why or why not?*
- *What if one table had 10 people and 5 pizzas and another had 3 people and 1 pizza? Would you decide where to sit by just choosing the one with the fewest people? Why or why not?*

Also consider asking students:

- *What is the ratio of pizza to people at the two tables?*
- *Can you scale these ratios so that they have a number in common?*
- *So, now which table gives you the most pizza?*
- *Can you scale the ratios so that the number of pizzas is equal to make the comparison easy?*
- *If you want to go to the table with the most pizza per person, at which table do you sit? How do $\frac{4}{10}$ pizza and $\frac{3}{8}$ pizza compare?*

Materials

- Student notebooks

ACE Assignment Guide
for Problem 2.2

Differentiated Instruction
Solutions for All Learners

Core 4, 5, 22
Other *Connections* 14–18; unassigned choices
from previous problems

Adapted For suggestions about adapting ACE
exercises, see the CMP *Special Needs Handbook*.
Connecting to Prior Units 14–17: *Bits and Pieces I*;
18: *Stretching and Shrinking*

Answers to Problem 2.2

A. No. Because 4 to 10 and 16 to 40 are equivalent ratios; and 3 to 8 and 15 to 40 are equivalent ratios, we can see that sitting at the large
table gives a person more pizza since 16 to 40
is greater than 15 to 40.

If students use unit rates, they may give the
following argument: Those at the large table
will get $\frac{4}{10}$, or $\frac{2}{5}$, of a pizza per person. Those at
the small table will get $\frac{3}{8}$ of a pizza per person.
Similarly, at the large table there are 2.5 people
per pizza and at the small table there are
2.6666 . . . people per pizza. Each person at
the large table will get more pizza than people at the small table.

B. $\frac{3}{8}$ relates to the small table and means 3 pizzas
for 8 people. Since it makes no sense to add
people and pizza, $\frac{3}{8}$ is a part-to-part comparison.

C. 1. Six is the difference between the number of
seats and the number of pizzas at the large
table. Five is the difference between the
number of seats and pizzas at the small
table.

2. Variable answers at this stage. Part (3)
should make it clear that she is wrong.

3. The example given here makes this clear
since Selena's method would give
$10 - 9 = 1$ and $8 - 3 = 5$ and she would
choose the small table. Yet, the large table
has almost a whole pizza for each person.

4. Selena is wrong. It may occasionally
accidentally produce a correct answer, but
in such a problem, you need to make the
comparison based on what portion of a
pizza each person gets, not on differences.

D. 1. There are 16 large tables and 10 small
tables. The complexity in this problem is
that we have two ratios to deal with. A
large table seats 10 people and a small
table seats 8 people. One way to think
about the problem is to ask what one
"group" of tables, 8 large and 5 small,
would seat. This would seat
$80 + 40$ people, or 120 people. So we
need two "groups," which would be
16 large tables and 10 small tables.

2. $\frac{80}{240}$, or $\frac{1}{3}$

3. About 67%.

Goals

- Find equivalent ratios
- Further develop strategies for comparing ratios

If your students have already talked about the notion of scaling up or down and how this relates to what they know about finding equivalent fractions, just take a minute to review what they have noticed so far.

Launch 2.3

Use the Getting Ready to focus students on finding equivalent ratios through scaling up and down and its relationship to finding equivalent fractions. Help them to see that it is easier to have a sense of the relationship if the numbers in the ratio are as small as possible. In the Getting Ready, the example given has easy but large numbers ($\frac{100}{80}$). This is so that students can think about the process they use rather than getting hung up on the numbers.

- *How do you scale down this ratio to make it easier to understand?* (Divide both numbers by 10 to get 10 to 8; divide both numbers by 20 to get 5 to 4.)

- *What are some other ratios equivalent to this ratio in which the numbers are greater?* (Sample answers: multiply both by 2 to get 200 to 160; and multiply both by 10 to get 1,000 to 800.)

- *How is scaling ratios like finding equivalent fractions for $\frac{100}{80}$? How is it different?* [They are alike in that you multiply (or divide) both numbers by the same value; scaling ratios is different in that ratios may not be written in fraction form and do not necessarily represent part-to-whole relationships.]

Set the context for Problem 2.3. You can read the situation and the formulas with the students so that they see what the problem is about.

It works well to have the students do Questions A and B and break for a whole class discussion of these two parts before having students go on to the last two parts (perhaps for homework).

A Think-Pair-Share arrangement works well. Be sure that each student makes the tables called for so that they have their own work to review at home.

You might want to have each group write their table, answer, and strategies for the problem on chart paper so that the summary is easier.

Explore 2.3

Since this problem gives practice in making tables to show relationships among amounts of food for different numbers of chimps, it gives students who are struggling with these ideas a chance to sort things out. Students may choose table-making as a strategy for parts of the problem where it is not specified. This is a good strategy, but some students may come up with equally effective strategies that will provide alternatives. As you move around the room, notice what is giving students difficulty so that you can bring these ideas up in the summary after Questions A and B.

Also be on the lookout for other ways of thinking and strategies that students may be devising. Be sure to ask about these in the summary.

Suggested Questions If students in a pair or group are having difficulty, ask questions such as the following:

- *What differences do you notice in how the mix changes as a chimp moves from being a baby to a young adult to an older chimp?*

- *Suppose you are feeding two baby chimps. How much of each part of the mix will you need? What did you do to find the amounts of each part of the mix?*

- *After a few entries in your table, how can you use the patterns that you see?*

- *How much will the total amount of feed differ for two baby chimps compared to just one?*

Summarize 2.3

You may want to have each group write their tables on chart paper. It will be easy for them to report what they found and what they noticed in their table for Question A or other tables they choose as a solution strategy.

Call on a group to start the discussion by presenting their table and answers to Question A. Ask if there are any groups that noticed other patterns in the table.

- *What would you do to find the table entry for feeding 60 baby chimps?* (Multiply the entry for 10 chimps by 6, multiply the entry for 1 chimp by 60, or multiply other factors that give 60, like 20 chimps multiplied by 3.)

Do a similar thing with Question B. Be sure to let all ideas come out in the discussion.

Suggested Questions To pull the main mathematical ideas out, ask:

- *What is an efficient method of finding a ratio equivalent to a given ratio?* (Use what we know about equivalent fractions to multiply or divide each part of the ratio by the same number to scale up or down.)

- *How do you choose what to multiply or divide by?* (Since you are comparing two ratios, you need one of the quantities to be the same in each of the ratios. This is like finding common numerators or common denominators with fractions.)

Check for Understanding

The ratios for two grades are given.

Grade A: 210 girls to 240 boys

Grade B: 95 girls to 120 boys

- *Which grade level has the greatest ratio of girls to boys?*

The issue of difference as a method may come up and can be talked about again. If one only looks at differences between numbers of girls and

boys, Grade B would be selected. Scaling the Grade B ratio so that the number of boys is the same is easy. This method gives these ratios: Grade A: 210 to 240 and Grade B: 190 to 240. This clearly shows that Grade A has the greatest ratio of girls to boys.

Question C

This could be assigned for students to think about at home with a short discussion the next day or completed in class with the following discussion on the same day.

Suggested Questions Ask:

- *I do not see the quantities 3 and 2 in the recipe for the mix for young adults. What did Darla do to get these numbers?* (She scaled the ratio 6 to 4 to the equivalent ratio 3 to 2.)

Let a couple of students present their thinking to the class.

- *Is Darla or Lamar correct?* (Lamar has the correct answer because his fraction represents the amount of high-fiber nuggets in the total mix. Darla's answer represents a comparison between the high-fiber and the high-protein nuggets.)

- *Who can talk to us about their answer and strategy for part (2)?* (The ratio of high-fiber to high-protein is 4 to 2, or 2 to 1. This means that a basic recipe using the 2 to 1 ratio would contain 3 cups total. The fraction of the total that is high-fiber would be $\frac{2}{3}$.)

- *What about part (3)?* (In a zoo with a ratio of male chimps to female chimps of 5 to 4, a "group" is 9 chimps total. So the fraction of the chimps that is male is $\frac{5}{9}$.)

- *What about part (4)?* (If we know that $\frac{2}{3}$ of the chimps are female, then we know that the total for a "group" of chimps is 3, of which 2 are female. This means that 1 is a male. So the ratio of female chimps to male chimps in that zoo is 2 to 1.)

2.3 Finding Equivalent Ratios

Mathematical Goals

- Find equivalent ratios
- Further develop strategies for comparing ratios

Launch

Use the Getting Ready to focus students on finding equivalent ratios through scaling up and down and its relationship to finding equivalent fractions.

Assign Questions A and B. Then break for class discussion.

A Think-Pair-Share arrangement works well.

Materials

- Transparencies 2.3A and 2.3B
- Transparency markers (optional)
- Chart paper and markers (optional)

Vocabulary

- scaling up
- scaling down

Explore

If students are having difficulty, ask questions such as the following:

- *What differences do you notice in how the mix changes as a chimp moves from being a baby to a young adult to an older chimp?*
- *Suppose you are feeding two baby chimps. How much of each part of the mix will you need? What did you do to find the amounts?*
- *How can you use the patterns that you see in your table?*
- *How much will the total amount of feed differ for two baby chimps compared to just one?*

Summarize

Consider having each group write on chart paper for reporting ease.

To pull the main mathematical ideas out, ask:

- *What is an efficient method of finding a ratio equivalent to a given ratio?*
- *How do you choose what to multiply or divide by?*

Check for Understanding

- *If the ratio for Grade A is 210 girls to 240 boys and the ratio for Grade B is 95 girls to 120 boys, which grade level has the greater proportion of girls?*

Consider asking:

- *I do not see the quantities 3 and 2 in the recipe for the mix for young adults. What did Darla do to get these numbers?*
- *Is Darla or Lamar correct?*

Materials

- Student notebooks

ACE Assignment Guide for Problem 2.3

Differentiated Instruction
Solutions for All Learners

Core 6–8, 21, 24
Other *Connections* 19, 20; *Extensions* 23; unassigned choices from previous problems
Adapted For suggestions about adapting ACE exercises, see the CMP *Special Needs Handbook*.
Connecting to Prior Units 19: *Bits and Pieces I*; 20: *Bits and Pieces III*; 21: *Bits and Pieces II*

Answers to Problem 2.3

A. 1. Dietary Needs of Baby Chimps

Number of chimps	1	2	3	4	5	10
Cups of high-fiber nuggets	2	4	6	8	10	20
Cups of high-protein nuggets	3	6	9	12	15	30

2. The cups of high-fiber nuggets increase at a rate of 2 cups per each additional chimp while the cups of high-protein nuggets increase at a rate of 3 cups per each additional chimp. The ratios are scaled up by consecutive integers based on the number of chimps. If you need to feed four chimps, multiply $2 \times 4 = 8$ for cups of high-fiber nuggets and $3 \times 4 = 12$ for cups of high-protein nuggets.

3. Since the ratio is 2 high-fiber to 3 high-protein, we can divide the 48 cups of high-fiber nuggets by 3 to get 16 cups and multiply 16 by 2 to get 32. The ratio of 32 to 48 is the same as the ratio of 2 to 3.

4. Since 125 represents the total, we have to find a way to sort out the parts. We have a ratio of 2 to 3, so we need 5 parts. $125 \div 5 = 25$ for each part. We know that the high-fiber is 2 parts, so there are 50 cups.

B. 1. 6 to 4, or 3 to 2

2. For each additional young-adult chimp, the cups of high-fiber nuggets increase by 6, and the cups of high-protein nuggets increase by 4. To find the number of cups of each type of nugget that is needed, multiply the cups of each for just one chimp by the number of chimps. To feed 21 chimps, you need

$6 \times 21 = 126$ cups of high-fiber nuggets and $4 \times 21 = 84$ cups of high-protein nuggets. The ratios remain the same, 6 to 4. Some students may make a table to solve this one.

Dietary Needs of Young Adult Chimps

Number of chimps	1	2	3	4	. . .	21
Cups of high-fiber nuggets	6	12	18	24	. . .	126
Cups of high-protein nuggets	4	8	12	16	. . .	84

3. We have 108 cups of high-fiber to 72 cups of high-protein nuggets (a total of 180 cups) for 18 chimps. We need to scale the ratio 108 : 72 to find the food mix for 3 chimps. 108 and 72 have many common factors. We can examine the common factors of 108 and 72 and see whether we can find a scaling factor that will give us a total of the 30 cups of food needed for 3 young-adult chimps per day. The common factors are 1, 2, 3, 4, 6, 9, 12, 18, 36. Dividing by each of these, we find that scaling down by a factor of 6 gives 18 : 12 which gives the 30 cups needed.

A second solution strategy is to divide each of the parts of the ratio by 18, the number of chimps the mix will feed, and then multiply by 3 because we need food for three chimps. Dividing by 18 and multiplying the result by 3 is the same thing as dividing by 6.

C. 1. Lamar is correct because his fraction represents the amount of high-fiber nuggets in the total mix. Darla's answer represents a comparison between the high-fiber and the high-protein nuggets.

2. The ratio of high-fiber to high-protein nuggets is 4 to 2, or 2 to 1. A batch using the 2 to 1 ratio contains 3 cups total. The fraction of the total that is high-fiber is $\frac{2}{3}$.

3. The fraction of chimps that is male is $\frac{5}{9}$.

4. If $\frac{2}{3}$ of the chimps in the zoo are female, then in a group of 3 chimps, 2 are females and 1 is male. So the ratio of female to male chimps is 2 to 1.

The student edition pages for this investigation begin on the next page.

Notes _____

_____

_____

_____

Investigation 2

Comparing Ratios, Percents, and Fractions

You used ratios, fractions, percents, and differences to compare quantities in Investigation 1. Now, you will develop strategies for choosing and using an appropriate comparison strategy. As you work through the problems, you will make sense of the statements in the *Did You Know?*

Did You Know?

- In 2001, 20.8% of all radio stations in the United States had country music as their primary format, while only 4.5% had a Top-40 format.

- For the first 60 miles of depth, the temperature of Earth increases 1°F for every 100 to 200 feet.

- In 2000, cancer accounted for about $\frac{1}{5}$ of all deaths in the United States.

- In 2001, silver compact cars and silver sports cars outsold black cars by a ratio of 5 to 3.

Go Online
PHSchool.com **For:** Information about any of these topics
Web Code: ane-9031

18 Comparing and Scaling

STUDENT PAGE

Notes _____

_____

_____

_____

2.1 Mixing Juice

Julia and Mariah attend summer camp. Everyone at the camp helps with the cooking and cleanup at meal times.

One morning, Julia and Mariah make orange juice for all the campers. They plan to make the juice by mixing water and frozen orange-juice concentrate. To find the mix that tastes best, they decide to test some mixes.

Mix A
2 cups concentrate   3 cups cold water

Mix B
5 cups concentrate   9 cups cold water

Mix C
1 cup concentrate   2 cups cold water

Mix D
3 cups concentrate   5 cups cold water

Problem 2.1 Developing Comparison Strategies

A. Which mix will make juice that is the most "orangey"? Explain.

B. Which mix will make juice that is the least "orangey"? Explain.

C. Which comparison statement is correct? Explain.

$\frac{5}{9}$ of Mix B is concentrate. $\frac{5}{14}$ of Mix B is concentrate.

D. Assume that each camper will get $\frac{1}{2}$ cup of juice.

  1. For each mix, how many batches are needed to make juice for 240 campers?

  2. For each mix, how much concentrate and how much water are needed to make juice for 240 campers?

E. For each mix, how much concentrate and how much water are needed to make 1 cup of juice?

ACE Homework starts on page 24.

Investigation 2 Comparing Ratios, Percents, and Fractions   **19**

Notes _____

_____

_____

_____

(19) 46

2.2 Sharing Pizza

The camp dining room has two kinds of tables. A large table seats ten people. A small table seats eight people. On pizza night, the students serving dinner put four pizzas on each large table and three pizzas on each small table.

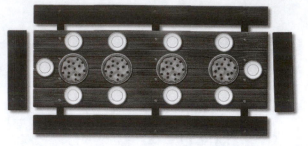

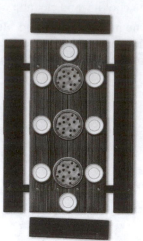

Problem 2.2 More Comparison Strategies

A. Suppose the pizzas are shared equally by everyone at the table. Does a person sitting at a small table get the same amount as a person sitting at a large table? Explain your reasoning.

B. Which table relates to $\frac{3}{8}$? What do the 3 and the 8 mean? Is $\frac{3}{8}$ a part-to-whole comparison or a part-to-part comparison?

C. Selena thinks she can decide at which table a person gets the most pizza. She uses the following reasoning:

$10 - 4 = 6$ and $8 - 3 = 5$ so the large table is better.

1. What does the 6 mean and what does the 5 mean in Selena's method of reasoning?

2. Do you agree or disagree with Selena's method?

3. Suppose you put nine pizzas on the large table. What answer does Selena's method give? Does this answer make sense?

4. What can you now say about Selena's method?

20   Comparing and Scaling

STUDENT PAGE

Notes _____

_____

_____

_____

D. 1. The ratio of large tables to small tables in the dining room is 8 to 5. There are exactly enough seats for the 240 campers. How many tables of each kind are there?

2. What fraction of the campers sit at small tables?

3. What percent of the campers sit at large tables?

ACE Homework starts on page 24.

2.3 Finding Equivalent Ratios

It is often helpful, when forming ratios, to replace the actual numbers being compared with simpler numbers that have the same relationship to each other.

- People prefer Bolda Cola over Cola Nola by a ratio of 17,139 to 11,426, or 3 to 2.

- Students prefer television to radio by a ratio of 100 to 50, or 2 to 1.

- Monthly sales of *Reader's Digest* magazine exceed those of *National Geographic* by 11,044,694 to 6,602,650, or about 3 to 2.

Getting Ready for Problem 2.3

Suppose all classes at your grade level took the cola taste test. The result was 100 to 80 in favor of Bolda Cola.

- How do you scale down this ratio to make it easier to understand?

- What are some other ratios equivalent to this ratio in which the numbers are greater? Finding greater numbers is scaling *up* the ratio.

- How is scaling ratios like finding equivalent fractions for $\frac{100}{80}$? How is it different?

Investigation 2 Comparing Ratios, Percents, and Fractions **21**

Notes _____

_____

_____

_____

Problem 2.3 Scaling Ratios

One of Ming's tasks at the county zoo's primate house is to mix food for the chimpanzees. The combination of high-fiber nuggets and high-protein nuggets changes as the chimps grow from babies to adults.

Ming has formulas for mixing high-fiber and high-protein nuggets for the chimps.

- Baby chimps: 2 cups high-fiber nuggets and 3 cups high-protein nuggets per serving
- Young adult chimps: 6 cups high-fiber nuggets and 4 cups high-protein nuggets per serving
- Older chimps: 4 cups high-fiber nuggets and 2 cups high-protein nuggets per serving

A. 1. What amounts of high-fiber and high-protein nuggets will Ming need when she has to feed 2 baby chimps? 3 baby chimps? 4 baby chimps?

Copy and complete the table below.

Dietary Needs of Baby Chimps

Number of Baby Chimps	1	2	3	4	5	10
Cups of High-Fiber Nuggets	■	■	■	■	■	■
Cups of High-Protein Nuggets	■	■	■	■	■	■

2. What patterns do you see in your table?

3. Ming puts 48 cups of high-protein nuggets into the baby chimp mix. How many cups of high-fiber nuggets does she put into the mix? Explain.

4. Ming has a total of 125 cups of mix for baby chimps. How many cups of high-fiber nuggets are in the mix? Explain.

B. 1. What is the ratio of high-fiber to high-protein nuggets for young adult chimps?

2. Scale this ratio up to show the ratio of high-fiber to high-protein nuggets that will feed 21 young adult chimps.

3. To feed 18 young adults, you need 108 cups of high-fiber nuggets and 72 cups of high-protein nuggets. Show how to scale down this ratio to feed 3 young adult chimps.

Notes

C. 1. Darla wants to compare the amount of high-fiber nuggets to the total amount of food mix for young adult chimps. She makes this claim:

"High-fiber nuggets are $\frac{3}{2}$ of the total."

Lamar says Darla is wrong. He makes this claim:

"High-fiber nuggets are $\frac{3}{5}$ of the total."

Who is correct? Explain.

2. What fraction of the total amount of food mix for older chimps is high-fiber nuggets?

3. Suppose the ratio of male chimps to female chimps in a zoo is 5 to 4. What fraction of the chimps are male?

4. Suppose $\frac{2}{3}$ of the chimps in a zoo are female. Find the ratio of female chimps to male chimps in that zoo.

ACE Homework starts on page 24.

Investigation 2 Comparing Ratios, Percents, and Fractions   **23**

Notes _____

_____

_____

_____

Applications

As you work on the ACE exercises, try a variety of reasoning methods. Then think about conditions when each method seems most helpful.

1. Compare these four mixes for apple juice.

Mix W	
5 cups concentrate	8 cups cold water

Mix X	
3 cups concentrate	6 cups cold water

Mix Y	
6 cups concentrate	9 cups cold water

Mix Z	
3 cups concentrate	5 cups cold water

a. Which mix would make the most "appley" juice?

b. Suppose you make a single batch of each mix. What fraction of each batch is concentrate?

c. Rewrite your answers to part (b) as percents.

d. Suppose you make only 1 cup of Mix W. How much water and how much concentrate do you need?

2. Examine these statements about the apple juice mixes in Exercise 1. Decide whether each is accurate. Give reasons for your answers.

a. Mix Y has the most water, so it will taste least "appley."

b. Mix Z is the most "appley" because the difference between the concentrate and water is 2 cups. It is 3 cups for each of the others.

c. Mix Y is the most "appley" because it has only $1\frac{1}{2}$ cups of water for each cup of concentrate. The others have more water per cup.

d. Mix X and Mix Y taste the same because you just add 3 cups of concentrate and 3 cups of water to turn Mix X into Mix Y.

24 Comparing and Scaling

Notes _____

_____

_____

_____

3. If possible, change each comparison of concentrate to water into a ratio. If not possible, explain why.

   a. The mix is 60% concentrate.

   b. The fraction of the mix that is water is $\frac{3}{5}$.

   c. The difference between the amount of concentrate and water is 4 cups.

4. At camp, Miriam uses a pottery wheel to make three bowls in 2 hours. Duane makes five bowls in 3 hours.

   a. Who makes bowls faster, Miriam or Duane?

   b. At the same pace, how long will it take Miriam to make a set of 12 bowls?

   c. At the same pace, how long will it take Duane to make a set of 12 bowls?

5. Guests at a pizza party are seated at 3 tables. The small table has 5 seats and 2 pizzas. The medium table has 7 seats and 3 pizzas. The large table has 12 seats and 5 pizzas. The pizzas at each table are shared equally. At which table does a guest get the most pizza?

6. For each business day, news reports tell the number of stocks that gained (went up in price) and the number that declined (went down in price). In each of the following pairs of reports, determine which is better news for investors.

   Homework Help Online
   PHSchool.com
   For: Help with Exercise 6
   Web Code: ane-3206

   a. [Gains outnumber declines by a ratio of 5 to 3.]   OR   [Gains outnumber declines by a ratio of 7 to 5.]

   b. [Gains outnumber declines by a ratio of 9 to 5.]   OR   [Gains outnumber declines by a ratio of 6 to 3.]

   c. [Declines outnumber gains by a ratio of 10 to 7.]   OR   [Declines outnumber gains by a ratio of 6 to 4.]

Investigation 2 Comparing Ratios, Percents, and Fractions   **25**

Notes _____

_____

_____

_____

7. Suppose a news story about the Super Bowl claims "Men outnumbered women in the stadium by a ratio of 9 to 5." Does this mean that there were 14 people in the stadium—9 men and 5 women? If not, what does the statement mean?

8. **Multiple Choice** Which of the following is a correct interpretation of the statement "Men outnumbered women by a ratio of 9 to 5?"

   A. There were four more men than women.

   B. The number of men was 1.8 times the number of women.

   C. The number of men divided by the number of women was equal to the quotient of $5 \div 9$.

   D. In the stadium, five out of nine fans were women.

Connections

9. If possible, change each comparison of red paint to white paint to a percent comparison. If it is not possible, explain why.

   a. The fraction of a mix that is red paint is $\frac{1}{4}$.

   b. The ratio of red to white paint in a different mix is 2 to 5.

10. If possible, change each comparison to a fraction comparison. If it is not possible, explain why.

    a. The nut mix has 30% peanuts.

    b. The ratio of almonds to other nuts in the mix is 1 to 7.

11. Find a value that makes each sentence correct.

   a. $\frac{3}{15} = \frac{\blacksquare}{30}$ **b.** $\frac{1}{2} < \frac{\blacksquare}{20}$

   c. $\frac{\blacksquare}{20} > \frac{3}{5}$ **d.** $\frac{9}{30} \leq \frac{\blacksquare}{15}$

   e. $\frac{\blacksquare}{12} \geq \frac{3}{4}$ **f.** $\frac{9}{21} = \frac{12}{\blacksquare}$

STUDENT PAGE

Notes _____

_____

_____

_____

12. Use the table to answer parts (a)–(e).

Participation in Walking for Exercise

	Ages 12–17	Ages 55–64
People Who Walk	3,781,000	8,694,000
Total in Group	23,241,000	22,662,000

SOURCE: U.S. Census Bureau. Go to PHSchool.com for a data update. Web Code: ang-9041

a. What percent of the 55–64 age group walk for exercise?

b. What percent of the 12–17 age group walk for exercise?

c. Write a ratio statement to compare the number of 12- to 17-year-olds who walk to the number of 55- to 64-year-olds who walk. Use approximate numbers to simplify the ratio.

d. Write a ratio statement to compare the percent of 12- to 17-year-olds who walk for exercise to the percent of 55- to 64-year-olds who walk for exercise.

e. Which data—actual numbers of walkers or percents—would you use in comparing the popularity of exercise walking among various groups? Explain.

13. The probability of getting a sum of 5 when you roll two number cubes is $\frac{4}{36}$. How many times should you expect to get a sum of 5 if you roll the cubes each number of times?

a. 9   **b.** 18   **c.** 27   **d.** 100   **e.** 450

14. For each diagram, write three statements comparing the areas of the shaded and unshaded regions. In one statement, use fraction ideas to express the comparison. In the second, use percent ideas. In the third, use ratio ideas.

a. 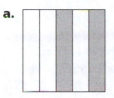   **b.**

15. Multiple Choice Choose the value that makes $\frac{18}{30} = \frac{\blacksquare}{15}$ correct.

F. 7   **G.** 8   **H.** 9   **J.** 10

16. Multiple Choice Choose the value that makes $\frac{\blacksquare}{15} \leq \frac{3}{5}$ correct.

A. 9   **B.** 10   **C.** 11   **D.** 12

Notes

17. Find a value that makes each sentence correct. Explain your reasoning in each case.

a. $\frac{3}{4} = \frac{\blacksquare}{12}$ b. $\frac{3}{4} < \frac{\blacksquare}{12}$ c. $\frac{3}{4} > \frac{\blacksquare}{12}$ d. $\frac{9}{12} = \frac{12}{\blacksquare}$

Go Online
PHSchool.com
For: Multiple-Choice Skills Practice
Web Code: ana-3254

18. The sketches show floor plans for dorm rooms for two students and for one student.

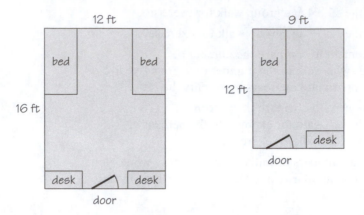

a. Are the floor plans similar rectangles? If so, what is the scale factor? If not, why not?

b. What is the ratio of floor areas of the two rooms (including space under the beds and desks)?

c. Which type of room gives more space per student?

19. Find values that make each sentence correct.

a. $\frac{6}{14} = \frac{\blacksquare}{21} = \frac{\blacksquare}{28}$ b. $\frac{\blacksquare}{27} = \frac{8}{36} = \frac{\blacksquare}{63}$

c. $\frac{\blacksquare}{20} = \frac{\blacksquare}{25} = \frac{6}{30}$ d. $\frac{\blacksquare}{8} = \frac{15}{\blacksquare} = \frac{24}{32}$

20. Suppose a news story reports, "90% of the people in the Super Bowl stadium were between the ages of 25 and 55." Alicia thinks this means only 100 people were in the stadium, and 90 of them were between 25 and 55 years of age. Do you agree with her? If not, what does the statement mean?

21. Suppose a news story reports, "A survey found that $\frac{4}{7}$ of all Americans watched the Super Bowl on television." Bishnu thinks this means the survey reached seven people and four of them watched the Super Bowl on television. Do you agree with him? If not, what does the statement mean?

28   Comparing and Scaling

Notes _____

_____

_____

_____

Extensions

22. Mammals vary in the length of their pregnancies, or gestations. *Gestation* is the time from conception to birth. Use the table to answer the questions that follow.

Gestation Times and Life Spans of Selected Mammals		
Animal	Gestation (days)	Life Span (years)
Chipmunk	31	6
Cat	63	12
Fox	52	7
Lion	100	15
Black Bear	219	18
Gorilla	258	20
Moose	240	12
Giraffe	425	10
Elephant (African)	660	35

SOURCE: *The World Almanac and Book of Facts*

a. Plan a way to compare life span and gestation time for animals and use it with the data.

b. Which animal has the greatest ratio of life span to gestation time? Which has the least ratio?

c. Plot the data on a coordinate graph using (*gestation, life span*) as data points. Describe any interesting patterns that you see. Decide whether there is any relation between the two variables. Explain how you reached your conclusion.

d. What pattern would you expect to see in a graph if each statement were true?

   i. Longer gestation time implies longer life span.

   ii. Longer gestation time implies shorter life span.

Connections   Extensions

STUDENT PAGE

Investigation 2 Comparing Ratios, Percents, and Fractions   **29**

Notes _____

_____

_____

_____

23. The city of Spartanville runs two summer camps—the Green Center and the Blue Center. The table below shows recent attendance at the two camps.

	Green	Blue
Boys	125	70
Girls	75	30

In this exercise, you will show how several approaches can be used to answer the following question.

> Which center seems to offer a camping program that appeals best to girls?

a. What conclusion would you draw if you focused on the differences between the numbers of boy and girl campers from each center?

b. How could you use fractions to compare the appeal of the two centers' camping programs for boys and girls? What conclusion would you draw?

c. How could you use percents to compare the appeal of the two centers' camping programs for boys and girls? What conclusion would you draw?

d. How could you use ratios to compare the appeal of the two centers' camping programs for boys and girls? What conclusion would you draw?

30 Comparing and Scaling

Notes _____

_____

_____

_____

24. Use the table below.

**Participation in Team Sports
at Springbrook Middle School**

Sport	Girls	Boys
Basketball	30	80
Football	10	60
Soccer	120	85
Total Surveyed	160	225

a. In which sport do boys most outnumber girls?

b. In which sport do girls most outnumber boys?

c. The participation in these team sports is about the same for
students at Key Middle School.

   i. Suppose 250 boys at Key play sports. How many would you
      expect to play each of the three sports?

   ii. Suppose 240 girls at Key play sports. How many would you
       expect to play each of the three sports?

Investigation 2 Comparing Ratios, Percents, and Fractions   **31**

Notes _____

_____

_____

_____

Mathematical Reflections 2

In this investigation, you solved problems by comparing ratios, percents, and fractions. You also used ratio, percent, and fraction data to solve problems of larger or smaller scale. The following questions will help you summarize what you have learned.

Think about your answers to these questions. Discuss your ideas with other students and your teacher. Then write a summary of your findings in your notebook.

1. The director of a recreation center wants to compare the 10 boys to the 20 girls who attend its camping program.

   a. How would you make a comparison using fractions?

   b. How would you make a comparison using percents?

   c. How would you make a comparison using ratios?

   d. How is your percent comparison related to your ratio comparison?

   e. How is your fraction comparison related to your percent comparison?

2. **a.** Explain how you would scale up the ratio 10 boys to 14 girls to find equivalent ratios.

   b. Explain how you would scale down the ratio 10 boys to 14 girls to find equivalent ratios.

Notes _____

_____

_____

_____

STUDENT PAGE

Investigation ②

ACE Assignment Choices

Differentiated Instruction
Solutions for All Learners

Problem 2.1
Core 1–3, 9, 10
Other *Connections* 11–13

Problem 2.2
Core 4, 5, 22
Other *Connections* 14–18; unassigned choices from previous problems

Problem 2.3
Core 6–8, 21, 24
Other *Connections* 19, 20; *Extensions* 23; unassigned choices from previous problems

Adapted For suggestions about adapting Exercise 1 and other ACE exercises, see the CMP *Special Needs Handbook*.
Connecting to Prior Units 9–11, 14–17, 19: *Bits and Pieces I*; 13: *How Likely Is It?*; 18: *Stretching and Shrinking*; 20: *Bits and Pieces III*; 21: *Bits and Pieces II*

Applications

1. **a.** Mix Y is the most appley given it has the highest concentrate to juice ratio. The ratios of concentrate to juice are the following: Mix W = 5 : 13, Mix X = 3 : 9, Mix Y = 6 : 15, and Mix Z = 3 : 8. One possible strategy: If you changed these (part–whole ratios) to percents you will find Mix Y has the greatest percent of concentrate at 40%, whereas Mix W's percent is about 38.5%, Mix X's is about 33.3%, and Mix Z's is 37.5%.

   b. Mix W = $\frac{5}{13}$, Mix X = $\frac{3}{9}$ = $\frac{1}{3}$, Mix Y = $\frac{6}{15}$ = $\frac{2}{5}$, Mix Z = $\frac{3}{8}$.

   c. Mix W ≈ 38.5%, Mix X ≈ 33.3%, Mix Y = 40%, Mix Z = 37.5%

   d. Mix W: $\frac{8}{13}$ cup water and $\frac{5}{13}$ cup concentrate

2. **a.** Not accurate since both water and concentrate contribute to the least appley taste. A mix with 9 cups of water that had 1 cup of concentrate would taste much less appley.

   b. Not accurate. Mix Y is the most appley. Also, being the most appley is not dependent on the difference between the two ingredients, but the fraction or percent of concentrate of the total cups of liquid.

   c. Accurate. Mix Y is the most appley because it has the greatest ratio of concentrate to water.

   d. Not accurate. The taste is determined by the ratio of concentrate to water. Since Mix Y has more concentrate per water it will have the most appley taste.

3. **a.** 6 : 4, or 3 : 2

   b. 2 : 3

   c. Not possible. This is discussing difference and to make a ratio, one would also have to know one of the amounts. Differences can be the same even when ratios between two quantities are different.

4. **a.** Duane. He can make about 1.7 (5 ÷ 3) bowls per hour and Miriam can make only 1.5 bowls per hour.

   b. 8 hours because $\frac{2}{3}$ = $\frac{8}{12}$.

   c. It will take Duane a little over 7 hours, or about 7.2 hours to make 12 bowls. Possible strategy: 5 ÷ 3 ≈ $1\frac{2}{3}$ and 12 ÷ $1\frac{2}{3}$ ≈ 7.2.

5. The medium table; at the medium table, each person gets about $\frac{3}{7}$, or 43%, of a pizza. In other words, there are about 2.3 people per pizza. At the small table, each person gets only $\frac{2}{5}$, or 40%, of a pizza. There are 2.5 people per

ACE ANSWERS 2

pizza. At the large table, each person gets about $\frac{5}{12}$, or 42%, of a pizza. There are 2.4 people per pizza.

6. a. The ratio of 5 to 3 is better than 7 to 5 for investors. In the ratio of 5 to 3, 5 out of every 8 people (0.625 or 62.5%) gain whereas with the ratio 7 to 5, 7 out of every 12 people (0.58333 or 58.3%) gain. Another way to look at it is the ratio of $5 : 3 = 1.6667$ and the ratio $7 : 5 = 1.4$.

   b. The ratio of $6 : 3$ is better than $9 : 5$. ($\frac{6}{9} > \frac{9}{14}$, 67% > 64%).

   c. The ratio of 10 to 7 is better for investors. $\frac{7}{17} \approx 41\%$ whereas $\frac{4}{10} = 40\%$.

7. No, but if there had been only 14 people, then 9 would have been male and 5 would have been female. It means for every 9 men in the entire stadium, there were 5 females. So if there were 9,000 males, there were 5,000 females.

8. B

Connections

9. a. 25% red paint   **b.** 28.6% red paint

10. a. $\frac{3}{10}$ peanuts   **b.** $\frac{1}{8}$ almonds

11. a. 6

   b. 11, or any decimal or fraction greater than 10.

   c. 13, or any decimal or fraction greater than 12.

   d. 4.5, or a greater number.

   e. 9, or a greater number.

   f. 28

12. a. About 38.4%. (8,694,000 ÷ 22,662,000)

   b. About 16.3%. (3,781,000 ÷ 23,241,000)

   c. The ratio of 12- to 17-year-olds who walk for exercise to 55- to 64-year-olds who walk for exercise is 3,781 to 8,694, or about 4 to 9.

   d. The ratio of the percentage of 12- to 17-year-olds who walk for exercise to the percent of 55- to 64-year-olds who walk for exercise is 8 to 19.

   e. Percents, because the number sampled in each category is not the same number, therefore percents seem more appropriate to use so that the two categories can be compared, based on numbers out of 100.

13. a. 1   **b.** 2   **c.** 3

   d. 11.1 (about 11)   **e.** 50

14. a. $\frac{2}{5}$ of the square is shaded, so $\frac{3}{5}$ of the square is unshaded. 40% of the square is shaded, so 60% is unshaded. The ratio of the shaded part to the unshaded part is 2 to 3.

   b. $\frac{1}{9}$ of the square is shaded, so $\frac{8}{9}$ is unshaded. Approximately 11% of the square is shaded, so 89% is unshaded. The ratio of shaded to unshaded is 1 to 8.

15. H

16. A

17 a. 9. The scale factor is 3 (12 ÷ 4 = 3 and 3 × 3 = 9).

   b. 10. The numerator must be greater than 9 because $\frac{9}{12} = \frac{3}{4}$.

   c. 8. $\frac{3}{4} = \frac{9}{12}$, so the numerator must be less than 9.

   d. 16. The scale factor is $\frac{4}{3}$ (12 ÷ 9 = $\frac{4}{3}$ and $\frac{4}{3} \times 12 = 16$).

18. a. Yes. The scale factor between the large room and small room is 0.75. (The ratio is 4 : 3.)

   b. 192 : 108, or 16 : 9

   c. The room for one student, as it gives 108 square feet per person while the other room gives 192 ÷ 2 = 96 square feet per person.

19. a. $\frac{6}{14} = \frac{9}{21} = \frac{12}{28}$

   b. $\frac{6}{27} = \frac{8}{36} = \frac{14}{63}$

   c. $\frac{4}{20} = \frac{5}{25} = \frac{6}{30}$

   d. $\frac{6}{8} = \frac{15}{20} = \frac{24}{32}$

20. No. It means that 90%, or every 9 out of 10 people in the stadium, were between 25 and 55. There could have been 25,000 people in the stadium, in which case 22,500 would have been between the ages of 25 and 55 (25,000 × 0.9 = 22,500). However, if there were only 100 people, then Alicia would be right that 90 were between those ages. Percents put actual numbers into a number that means "out of 100" in order to give a means of comparison.

21. No. It means that for every 7 people that responded to the survey, 4 of them watched the Super Bowl. If the survey only sampled 7 people, then 4 of them watched. But if the survey sampled 7,000 people, about 4,000 watched. $\frac{4}{7}$ means that four sevenths of the number sampled, whatever that number is, watched. For example, if the survey sampled 100 people, $\frac{4}{7} \times 100$ would be 57.14.

Extensions

22. a. Ratios are a possible method of comparison. First change life span, which is measured by years, to be measured by days. This can be done by multiplying the number of years for life span by 365 (days). Then, change the ratios into decimals in order to compare (Figure 3).

b. The greatest life span to gestation time ratio is the chipmunk, which has a ratio of 2,190 to 31, or 70.6. The least life span to gestation time ratio is the giraffe, which has a ratio of 3,650 : 425, or 8.6.

c. Most of the coordinates follow the pattern that as gestation increases, life span increases. This is true except for two of the mammals, the moose and giraffe. From the pattern, there does appear to be a relationship between the gestation and the life span.

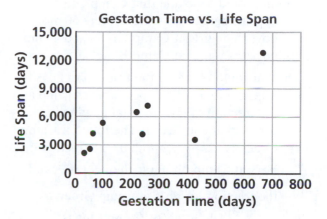

d. i. A positive slope, going up from the left to the right, to illustrate that as x (gestation) goes up/increases, y (life span) goes up/increases.

ii. A negative slope, going down from left to right, so as x, or gestation, goes up/increases, y (life span) goes down/decreases.

ACE ANSWERS

Figure 3

Gestation Times and Life Spans of Selected Mammals

Animal	Gestation (days)	Life Span (years)	Life Span (days)	Ratio of Life Span to Gestation (days)
Chipmunk	31	6	2,190	2,190 : 31, or 70.6
Cat	63	12	4,380	4,380 : 63, or 69.5
Fox	52	7	2,555	2,555 : 52, or 49.1
Lion	100	15	5,475	5,475 : 100, or 54.75
Black Bear	219	18	6,570	6,570 : 219, or 30
Gorilla	258	20	7,300	7,300 : 258, or 28.3
Moose	240	12	4,380	4,380 : 240, or 18.25
Giraffe	425	10	3,650	3,650 : 425, or 8.6
Elephant	660	35	12,775	12,775 : 660, or 19.4

23. Possible answers:

  a. The camps were relatively close in terms of the difference between boys and girls. The difference between the two camps was that 45 more girls attended Camp Green than Camp Blue and 55 more boys attended Camp Green than Camp Blue. Therefore, one could conclude that Camp Green appeals best to girls. There were 50 more boys than girls at Camp Green and 40 more boys than girls at Camp Blue.

  b. You could compute the fraction of boys to total numbers of campers at each camp and the fraction of girls to total numbers of campers at each camp. The total for Camp Green is $125 + 75 = 200$. The fraction of boys at Camp Green is then $\frac{125}{200} = \frac{5}{8}$, and the fraction for girls at Camp Green is $\frac{75}{200} = \frac{3}{8}$. The total for Camp Blue is $70 + 30 = 100$. The fraction of boys at Camp Blue is $\frac{70}{100} = \frac{7}{10}$, and the fraction for girls at Camp Blue is $\frac{30}{100} = \frac{3}{10}$. One can then compare fractions with like denominators, comparing $\frac{5}{8} = \frac{25}{40}$ for boys at Camp Green to $\frac{3}{8} = \frac{15}{40}$ for girls at Camp Green. $\frac{7}{10}$ and $\frac{3}{10}$ for Camp Blue become $\frac{28}{40}$ boys and $\frac{12}{40}$ girls for Camp Blue. One could then conclude that more girls prefer Camp Green and more boys prefer Camp Blue based on fractions of the total campers.

  c. 62.5% of campers at Camp Green were boys and 70% of campers at Camp Blue were boys. A conclusion could be that boys preferred Camp Blue to Camp Green. 37.5% of campers at Camp Green were female and 30% at Camp Blue were female. Girls preferred to attend Camp Green over Camp Blue.

  d. The ratio of 5 to 3 describes boys to girls at Camp Green and a ratio of 7 to 3 describes boys to girls at Camp Blue. The ratio of boys to girls is greater at Camp Blue than Camp Green.

24. a. Football (The ratio of boys to girls is 6 : 1, the greatest ratio of all the sports.)

  b. Soccer

  c. Numbers are rounded to nearest whole number.

    i. Basketball = 89, football = 67, soccer = 94.

    ii. Basketball = 45, football = 15, soccer = 180.

Possible Answers to Mathematical Reflections

1. Answers will vary. These are sample ones:

  a. $\frac{1}{3}$ of the students who attend the camping program are boys.

  b. About 33.333% of the students who attend the camping program are boys.

  c. The ratio of boys to girls is 1 to 2 (1 : 2).

  d. The percent comparison is related to the ratio comparison because the part-to-part relationship of boys to girls can sensibly be combined to make a part-to-whole relationship and then scaled to a percent, which is out of 100.

  e. The fraction of the boys is related to the percent comparison because it represents a part-to-whole relationship (the number of boys out of the total), which can then be scaled to a percent.

2. a. Multiply both numbers in the ratio by the same number.

  b. Divide both numbers in the ratio by the same number.

Mathematical and Problem-Solving Goals

- Examine and connect the idea of unit rates to what students already know about ratios and about linear relationships

- Further develop understanding of unit rates and how to compute and interpret them

- Work with the important application of rates to miles per hour (speed)

- Introduce the concept of "average" or "steady" rate of progress

- Introduce and formalize the meaning of unit rate and computation strategies for computing unit rates

- Relate unit rate to the slope of the line representing the equation of the underlying relationship

- Confront the issue of what it means to divide in rate situations

Summary of Problems

Problem 3.1 Technology on Sale

Students compare three different kinds of calculators with different prices. They use rate tables as a way of scaling rates up and down. Students also are asked the reverse: Given an amount to spend, how many calculators of a specified kind can be bought?

Problem 3.2 Time, Rate, and Distance

Students return to the familiar relationship of distance equals rate of speed times time ($d = rt$). Sascha bikes on a course that has hills and flat areas. Students compute how far Sascha travels and the time it takes him on each part of the course. Then they figure out what constant rate of speed equals Sascha's performance.

Problem 3.3 Comparing CD Prices

Students' unit rates are used to compare businesses selling CDs using different pricing schemes. The question is to figure out how many CDs have to be bought to make the Web site a bargain compared to each of the other options. This is actually solving a system of equations, but students will use informal methods to find a solution.

Problem 3.4 What Does Dividing Tell You?

Students learn that you can divide either number of a ratio into the other. If you have 12 people and 8 pizzas, $12 \div 8 = 1.5$ tells you that there are 1.5 people per pizza. If you compute $8 \div 12 = 0.\overline{6}$, this tells you that each person gets $\frac{2}{3}$ of a pizza. In rate terms, this is $\frac{2}{3}$ of a pizza per person. The same information is conveyed with the two unit rates, but the two rates are different and the labels are different.

	Suggested Pacing	Materials for Students	Materials for Teachers	ACE Assignments
All	$4\frac{1}{2}$ days	Graphing calculators, grid paper, blank transparencies and markers or chart paper and markers (optional), student notebooks	Transparency markers	
3.1	1 day		Transparencies 3.1A and 3.1B	1–3, 13–18, 33
3.2	1 day			4–8, 10, 19–23
3.3	1 day			9, 11, 24–26, 34
3.4	1 day		Transparencies 3.4A and 3.4B	12, 27–32
MR	$\frac{1}{2}$ day			

Goal

- Examine and connect the idea of unit rates to what students already know about ratios and about linear relationships

Launch 3.1

To introduce the topic of unit rates, go over the statements on the introductory page of Investigation 3. Here, several examples of rates are given. Use the Getting Ready to examine the statements given.

Suggested Questions Ask:

- *What two things are being compared in the rate statements?* (miles per gallon, sandwiches per person, dollars per hour, number of Calories per serving, and kilometers per hour)

- *Which of the rate statements given is different from the others?* (The "355 Calories per 6-ounce serving" seems different from the others because the unit is a 6-ounce serving. The students might want to see this as 59.1$\overline{6}$ Calories per serving. But one can also look at the real rate as 355 per serving and the 6 ounces as just specifying what a serving means.)

- *In which of the situations is a quantity being compared to one unit of another?* (In all the situations. Some students may question the 355 Calories per 6 oz serving. Here, one can think of the 6 oz serving as 1 serving and hence see this as a unit rate per serving.)

- *These are examples of rates that are called unit rates. A unit rate tells us how many per unit. Miles per hour tells how many miles are matched with 1 hour of travel and so on.*

- *What are some other rates that you have encountered?* (Varied responses. Examine several and ask someone other than the student who offers the idea to explain whether the example represents a rate. If so, ask the students what descriptors tell us what

kind of rate it is. Do two or three examples so that the class begins to see how a rate differs from a typical ratio that they have seen in earlier problems.)

- *Does the statement "440 mi traveled on 20 gal of gas" represent a unit rate? Why or why not?* (No, because it does not tell you how much per unit. If you knew miles traveled per gallon, it would be a unit rate.)

- *Can you find a related unit rate?* (Yes. It is 22 mi/gal.)

- *How did you find that?* (I divided the 440 mi by the 20 gal.)

- *Did anyone have a different way to think about this?* (Various answers.)

- *Now let's use this kind of thinking to help solve the challenge of buying calculators.*

Move into the problem by reading the ad for calculators with the students. Look at the mock-up for a rate table and discuss what a rate table tells you. Be sure that they see that they have made many tables that matched related variables before. Here we are looking at a special relationship called a rate. A rate also relates two variables that change in relationship to each other just as the examples in *Variables and Patterns* did. The ad for calculator sales will help focus students on the concept of unit rates. For many students, the natural way to compare the two offers is to find the two unit prices (or unit rates) and compare them.

Put students in groups of three or four to work on the problem. Suggest that each person make a rate table for Question A and then discuss their ideas and strategies.

Explore 3.1

As you circulate among the groups, ask questions to help students focus on the meaning of a unit rate and how it can be used to generate rate tables and rules.

Suggested Questions Ask questions, such as the following, to groups that are struggling:

- *Can you find out what a single calculator will cost? If so, how?*

- *How can you use your answer to help fill in the rate table?*

- *Do you see any patterns in your rate table? How would you describe them?*

- *Does the unit rate help you to write a rule that will predict the number of miles* m *for any number of gallons of gas* g*? If so, how? (*m = *unit rate* × g*)*

If students have difficulty writing the equations in Question F, have them state in words how they can use the unit rate to find the price for any number of calculators. Their verbal descriptions should lead them to the equations.

Summarize 3.1

Have groups share their findings. Examine the rate tables as a class, and ask students what patterns they see in the data. (This is a chance to review the representations that were studied in the *Variables and Patterns* unit.)

Suggested Questions

- *What patterns do you see in the tables?* (Here are some patterns students have noticed: Doubling the number of calculators doubles the price. Tripling the number of calculators triples the price. The change in price from one calculator to two calculators in the table is the same as the unit price for a calculator. To find the unit price or rate, just divide the total price by the number of calculators in the ads. This will tell you how much one costs. The table for Scientific and Graphing calculators increases much faster than the table for Fraction calculators.)

- *What would be the shape of the graphs of the data in these tables?* (They would be straight lines.)

- *How would the graphs be alike and different?* (Students should recognize that the graphs would be straight lines, but they would differ in the steepness with which they rise.)

Discuss each part of the problem. Questions C and D ask students to use their unit rates to figure out how many calculators can be bought for a given amount. Question F asks for an equation for each kind of calculator to compute the price for any number of calculators.

Going Further

Ask:

- *How can you write one equation to compute the price of any number of calculators of any kind?* (Students should see that the equations have the same form, just a different cost per calculator for each different kind. If they treat the cost per calculator as a variable, then they can write a single equation that will work for any number and any cost. They should get an equation such as $P = C \times N$ or $P = CN$, where P is the total price, C is the cost for each calculator, and N is the number bought.)

INVESTIGATION 3

Mathematical Goal

- Examine and connect the idea of unit rates to what students already know about ratios and about linear relationships

Launch

Go over the statements in the Getting Ready.

- *In each of these situations, what is being compared?*
- *In which of the situations is a quantity being compared to one unit of another?*

Explain *unit rates* and consider asking:

- *What are some other rates that you have encountered?*
- *Does the statement "440 mi traveled on 20 gal of gas" represent a unit rate? Why or why not?*
- *Could you find a related unit rate?*
- *How did you find that?*
- *Did anyone have a different way to think about this?*

Move into the problem by reading the ad for calculators with the students.

Look at the mock-up for a rate table and discuss what a rate table tells you.

Have students work in groups of three or four.

Materials

- Transparencies 3.1A and 3.1B
- Transparency markers (optional)

Explore

As you circulate, ask the following to struggling groups:

- *Can you find out what a single calculator will cost? If so, how?*
- *How can you use your answer to help fill in the rate table?*
- *Do you see any patterns in your rate table? How would you describe them?*
- *Does the unit rate help you to write a rule that will predict the number of miles for any number of gallons of gas? If so, how?*

Materials

- Graphing calculators
- Grid paper

Summarize

Have groups share their findings.

Examine the rate tables as a class.

- *What patterns do you see in the tables?*
- *What would be the shape of the graphs of the data in these tables?*
- *How would the graphs be alike and different?*

Discuss each part of the problem.

Materials

- Student notebooks

Vocabulary

- rates
- unit rate

ACE Assignment Guide for Problem 3.1

Differentiated Instruction Solutions for All Learners

Core 1–3, 33
Other *Connections* 13–18

Adapted For suggestions about adapting Exercises 1, 2, and other ACE exercises, see the CMP *Special Needs Handbook*.
Connecting to Prior Units 13–18: *Bits and Pieces II, Bits and Pieces III*

Answers to Problem 3.1

A. (Figure 4)

B. 53 fraction calculators = $318. Possible approach using the rate table: 53 calculators can be regrouped as 2 sets of 20, 1 set of 10 and 1 set of 3 calculators or $120 + $120 + $60 + $18 = $318.

27 scientific calculators = $432. Possible approach using the rate table: 27 calculators can be regrouped as 1 set of 20 calculators, a set of 5 calculators and 1 set of 2 calculators or $320 + $80 + $32 = $432.

9 graphing calculators = $720. Possible approach using the rate table: 9 calculators can be purchased as 1 set of 5 and 1 set of 4 calculators or $400 + $320 = $720.

C. A school can buy 65 fraction calculators with $390. Possible approach: Using the rate table, find the cost for multiple sets of 20 calculators. Three sets of 20, or 60 fraction calculators costs $360. Since fraction calculators are $6 each and there is $30 left to spend, another 5 calculators can be purchased for a total of 65 calculators. You can also divide $390 by $6, the cost of one calculator, to get the 65.

A school can buy 14 fraction calculators with $84. Possible approach: Use the rate table to find the cost of 10 calculators which is $60. Since fraction calculators are $6 each and there is $24 left to spend, another 4 calculators can be purchased for a total of 14 fraction calculators. You can also divide $84 by $6, the cost of one calculator.

D. A school can buy 31 graphing calculators with $2,500. Possible approach: Using the rate table, find the cost for multiple sets of calculators. You can buy 2 sets of 15 calculators for $2,400, leaving $80.00 to spend on 1 additional calculator. You will have $20 left over. You can also divide the total $2,500 by the cost per calculator or $80.

A school can buy 7 graphing calculators with $560. Possible approach: Using the rate table, a set of 5 calculators is $400. This leaves $160 that can be used to buy 2 more calculators for a total of 7 calculators. You can also divide $560 by $80 or the cost of one calculator.

E. Division

F. Possible answer: If n is the number of calculators purchased, p is the price for one calculator, and t is total price, then a general equation would be $n \times p = t$. Specific equations for each type of calculator are: $6n = t$ (fraction), $16n = t$ (scientific), and $80n = t$ (graphing). These equations work when purchasing a set with one type of calculator.

For the Teacher We are not expecting this here, but a student might write an equation for finding the cost of any combination of calculators. For example, if x = fraction, y = scientific, and z = graphing, then the equation $6x + 16y + 80z = total\ price$ will find the cost of combination of the three types of calculators.

Figure 4

Price of Calculators for Schools

Number of Calculators	1	2	3	4	5	10	15	20
Fraction	$6	$12	$18	$24	$30	$60	$90	$120
Scientific	$16	$32	$48	$64	$80	$160	$240	$320
Graphing	$80	$160	$240	$320	$400	$800	$1,200	$1,600

3.2 Time, Rate, and Distance

Goals

- Further develop understanding of unit rates and how to compute and interpret them
- Work with the important application of rates to miles per hour (speed)
- Introduce the concept of "average" or "steady" rate of progress

In Problem 3.2, information is given in descriptive form about Sascha's bicycle ride.

He traveled on a course that had hilly, flat, and downhill parts. These conditions affected the speed that Sascha could cycle. The parts of the problem focus on different aspects of how the course and his rate of speed relate.

Launch 3.2

Read or tell the story of Sascha's ride to the class. The information in the Did You Know? helps to raise interest in the context. You can also connect to their own experiences riding a bike.

Displaying the story of Sascha's ride and talking through what information is given can be done as a class, or you may decide to let each group make sense of the story for themselves. Whichever way you launch the problem, be sure that the students understand what the questions are asking, especially Questions C and D.

Have the students work on the problem in groups of two to four.

Explore 3.2

Suggested Questions If the students cannot find a way to get started, ask:

- *What exactly do you know about Sascha's trip?* (Get them to focus on elaborating exactly what they know. He traveled for 1 h and 24 min. He went 28 mi. At different points in the trip he was going different speeds.)

When the students have gotten somewhere on understanding what they know about Sascha's trip, ask:

- *Tell me in your own words what Question C (or Question D) is asking you to figure out.*
- *If I send two of you out of the room to go to the library to get a book, is it possible for you to each walk at different rates and get there at the same time? If so, give an example.* (Students may not immediately see that for this to happen the rates of at least one of the walkers must vary over parts of the distance. If this is the case, ask the next question.)
- *Could one of you walk at a steady rate over the entire distance and get there at the same time as someone walking for part of the time at a faster rate? If so, how?* (The average rate for time expended for one must equal that of the other.)
- *This situation is an interesting one since both the time and the distance have to be considered in answering Questions C and D. Each has to cover 28 miles in 84 minutes.*

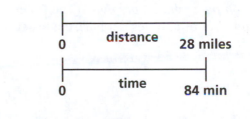

Summarize 3.2

Give groups a chance to talk about their answers and their strategies.

Suggested Questions Ask specifically for answers to questions such as the following:

- *How did you compute the rates in Question A?* (5 mi in 20 min is the same rate as 5 × 3 mi in 20 × 3 min, or 1 h. This scaling up to an hour gives 15 mi/h. 8 mi in 24 min can be scaled by the factor $\frac{60}{24} = \frac{5}{2}$ to get 8 × $\frac{5}{2}$ mi in 24 × $\frac{5}{2}$ min. This gives 20 mi in 60 min, or 20 mi/hour. Scale 15 mi in 40 min using the factor $\frac{60}{40} = \frac{3}{2}$ to get 15 × $\frac{3}{2}$ mi in 40 × $\frac{3}{2}$ min, or 22.5 mi/h.

- *What do your answers to Question A tell you?* (distance per unit of time for each part of the ride)

- *Do you think that his speed was constant throughout each time interval? Why or why not?* (No. It is hard to ride a bike at a steady rate. He likely had some variation in rate of speed over each time interval.)

- *Say in your own words what "average" rate of speed means.* (It means that if he rode at this rate of speed steadily throughout the time interval, he would have reached the same place at the same time.)

- *What does a steady rate of speed mean?* (Essentially the same thing as the average rate of speed. You maintain the same speed throughout the interval.)

Note that the idea of a steady rate is sometimes referred to as a constant speed.

- *How can you tell when he is going faster if you compute miles per minute?* (The greater the miles per minute, the faster he is going.)

- *How can you tell when he is going faster if you compute minutes per mile?* (The fewer the number of minutes per mile, the faster he is going.)

- *What computation did you perform to find how long it would take you to travel the 28 mi Sascha traveled if you are going 13 mi/h? Why?* (Divide 28 mi by 13 mi/h to get 2.15 hours.)

- *What strategy did you use to find a steady rate that would tie Sascha?* (Found the total time and the total distance and computed the rate at which he cycled. For example: divide $\frac{28 \text{ miles}}{1\frac{2}{5} \text{ hours}} = \frac{28}{1.4} = 20$ mi/h)

- *How can you match the parts of the trip to the conditions of the path? Explain.* (He would probably go fastest on the downhill portion, slowest on the uphill portion, and middling fast on the flat stretch. So you compute the rate of speed for each section. Part 1 is 15 mi/h; Part 2 is 20 mi/h; and Part 3 is 22.5 mi/h. So Part 1 was the slowest and probably uphill, Part 2 was the middle rate and probably on flat road, and Part 3 was the fastest and probably downhill.)

Mathematical Goals

- Further develop understanding of unit rates and how to compute and interpret them
- Work with the important application of rates to miles per hour (speed)
- Introduce the concept of "average" or "steady" rate of progress

Launch

Read or tell the story of Sascha's ride to the class.

Consider using the information in the Did You Know? or connect to their own experience of riding a bike.

Have the students work on the problem in groups of two to four.

Explore

For struggling students, consider asking:

- *What exactly do you know about Sascha's trip?*

When students have some understanding, consider asking:

- *Tell me in your own words what Question C (or Question D) is asking you to figure out.*
- *If I send two of you out of the room to go to the library to get a book, is it possible for you to each walk at different rates and get there at the same time? If so, give an example.*
- *Could one of you walk at a steady rate over the entire distance and get there at the same time as someone walking part of the time at a faster rate? If so, how?*

Materials

- Graphing calculators
- Grid paper

Summarize

Give groups a chance to talk about their answers and their strategies.

Ask the following:

- *How did you compute the rates in Question A?*
- *What do your answers to Question A tell you?*
- *Do you think that his speed was constant throughout each time interval? Why or why not?*
- *Say in your own words what "average" rate of speed means.*
- *What does a steady rate of speed mean?*
- *How can you tell when he is going faster if you compute miles per minute?*
- *How can you tell when he is going faster if you compute minutes per mile?*

Materials

- Student notebooks

continued on next page

- *What computation did you perform to find how long it would take you to travel the 28 mi Sascha traveled if you are going 13 mi/h? Why?*

- *What strategy did you use to find a steady rate that would tie Sascha?*

- *How can you match the parts of the trip to the conditions of the path? Explain.*

ACE Assignment Guide for Problem 3.2

Differentiated Instruction
Solutions for All Learners

Core 4–8
Other *Applications* 10; *Connections* 19–23; unassigned choices from previous problems

Adapted For suggestions about adapting ACE exercises, see the CMP *Special Needs Handbook*.
Connecting to Prior Units 23: *Bits and Pieces II, Bits and Pieces III, Variables and Patterns*

Answers to Problem 3.2

A. Part 1: 15 mi/h

Part 2: 20 mi/h

Part 3: 22.5 mi/h

B. 1. Part 3 is the fastest, and Part 1 is the slowest.

2. The answers in Question A give how many miles Sascha could have gone in 1 h. The greatest miles per hour would be the fastest part, and the least miles per hour would be the slowest part.

C. 2.15 h, or 2 hours and 9 minutes

D. 20 mi/h

3.3 Comparing CD Prices

Goals

- Introduce and formalize the meaning of unit rate and computation strategies for computing unit rates

- Relate unit rate to the slope of the line representing the equation of the underlying relationship

  This section formalizes the meaning of unit rate, formalizes computation strategies for computing unit rates, and relates unit rate to the slope of the line representing the equation of the underlying relationship. Students have found unit rates in the earlier problems, but here there is a direct focus on the concept and strategy for finding, interpreting, and using a unit rate to compare or describe situations.

Launch 3.3

Read over the information in the advertisements with the class.

Suggested Questions Ask such questions as:

- *What would you ask yourselves if you saw such ads? (Which is the less expensive deal? From which store can I get the most for my money?)*

- *These are the kinds of questions you will be asking and solving in the problem. Be sure to keep records of your thinking so that you can justify your reasoning in our summary.*

In Questions B and C, students are asked to write equations (rules) that can be used to calculate the price for purchases of CDs. Remind them:

- *Sometimes it helps to write statements for specific numbers of CDs and the price so that you can get a sense of what operations you use every time. This can help you to see a pattern and then write an equation for each store so that you can compute the price for any number of CDs.*

Either go over the text for all five questions, or at least warn the students that Question D introduces yet another choice of ways to buy CDs.

You might want to point out that although Question C asks for sales tax, Question D does not. A Think-Pair-Share will work well.

Explore 3.3

As you circulate, pay attention to which pairs of students have good explanations for their ideas and who is struggling.

Suggested Questions For students struggling with writing equations suggest they write a statement for the price of one CD, two CDs, three CDs, and so on, or to make a table. Ask:

- *What are the variables in the situation, and what letters are good representations for the variables?*

- *Which seems to be the independent variable, and which the dependent variable?*

Then, suggest they look for patterns in their statements and see if they can write a general equation using variables to show how to compute prices for any number of CDs.

Summarize 3.3

Use the summary to review the ideas of *rate, unit rate, variables, independent, dependent, equation,* and making comparisons.

Suggested Questions Ask questions such as the following:

- *Explain what a rate is and give some examples of different kinds of rates.*

- *What does unit rate mean? What are some examples where a unit rate is useful?*

- *What variables were you dealing with in the various parts of the problem? How did you decide which was the independent and which was the dependent variable?*

- *How do the dependent and the independent variables show up in an equation?*

INVESTIGATION 3

- *What are some ways of making comparisons among the options for buying CDs?*

- *How did you figure out the answers to Question E?*

- *If you made a graph for numbers of CDs and prices for each of the three companies, what would each graph look like? Are they straight lines? Do they go through the origin?* (Music City and CD World go through the origin, but since the Web site has a fixed price up front, it would not go through the origin. All three are straight lines because the growth pattern for each is to add a constant for the next greater number of CDs.)

- *Think about the graphs or tables for the Web site and Music City. What do you see that would help answer Question E, part (1)? What about part (2)?* (Students may not see why the point of intersection on a graph or a table is the place where the Web site becomes the better buy. Don't worry about this now. This will come up again in *Moving Straight Ahead*. These questions are meant to raise students' curiosity for something they will study in more depth later.)

3.3 Comparing CD Prices

Mathematical Goals

- Introduce and formalize the meaning of unit rate and computation strategies for computing unit rates
- Relate unit rate to the slope of the line representing the equation of the underlying relationship

Launch

Together read over the information in the advertisements. Ask questions such as:

- *What would you ask yourselves if you saw such ads?*
- *These are the kinds of questions you will be asking and solving in the problem. Be sure to keep records of your thinking so that you can justify your reasoning in our summary.*

Go over the text for all four parts or warn students that Question D introduces yet another choice of ways to buy CDs.

Have students work in a Think-Pair-Share.

Explore

For students struggling, suggest they write a statement for the price of one CD, two CDs, three CDs, and so on, or make a table. Ask:

- *What are the variables in the situation and what letters would be good representations for them?*
- *Which seems to be the independent variable and which the dependent variable?*

Materials
- Graphing calculators
- Grid paper

Summarize

Review the ideas of *rate, unit rate, variables, independent, dependent, equation,* and making comparisons.

Ask questions such as the following:

- *Explain what a rate is and give some examples of different kinds of rates.*
- *What does unit rate mean? Give some examples where a unit rate is useful.*
- *What variables were you dealing with in the parts of the problem? How did you decide which was the independent and which the dependent variable?*
- *How do the dependent and the independent variables show up in an equation?*

Materials
- Student notebooks

Vocabulary
- rate
- unit rate
- variables
- independent variable
- dependent variable
- equation

continued on next page

- *What are some ways of making comparisons among the options for buying CDs?*
- *How did you figure out the answers to Question E?*
- *If you made a graph for numbers of CDs and prices for each of the three companies, what would each graph look like? Are they straight lines? Do they go through the origin?*
- *Think about the graphs or tables for the Web site and Music City. What do you see that would help answer Question E, part (1)? What about part (2)?*

ACE Assignment Guide
for Problem 3.3

Differentiated Instruction
Solutions for All Learners

Core 9, 11
Other *Connections* 24–26; *Extensions* 34; unassigned choices from previous problems

Adapted For suggestions about adapting ACE exercises, see the CMP *Special Needs Handbook*.
Connecting to Prior Units 24, 25: *Data About Us*

Answers to Problem 3.3

A. CD World has the lower price per CD. Music City is $9.99 per CD and CD World is $9.40 per CD.

B. Music City: $c = 9.99n$

   CD World: $c = 9.40n$

C. Music City: $c = 9.99n + 0.05(9.99n)$ or $c = 1.05(9.99n)$

   CD World: $c = 9.40n + 0.05(9.40n)$ or $c = 1.05(9.40n)$

D. $c = 8.99n + 5$

E.
Cost of CDs

Number of CDs Purchased	Web Site	Music City	CD World
1	13.99	10.49	9.87
2	22.98	20.98	19.74
3	31.97	31.47	29.61
4	40.96	41.96	39.48
5	49.95	52.45	49.35
6	58.94	62.94	59.22

1. 4 or more

2. 6 or more

What Does Dividing Tell You?

Goal

- Confront the issue of what it means to divide in rate situations

   In this section, students look at a variety of situations that can be solved by computing unit rates. The text asks questions that point toward the two different possibilities and helps students develop ways of reasoning about the labels of the quantities being divided to determine the label for the result. Interpreting what a division means in a given situation is not trivial for many students. For this reason we have added this additional focus directly on division and the meaning of that division.

Launch 3.4

Use the Getting Ready to engage students with the ideas. Read through the situation and the questions and give students a few minutes to think about the questions being asked. The first question is a key one. Here the character, Dario, has divided the two numbers for the CornerMarket prices in two different orders and has found two answers. Figuring out what each of the answers for the division results mean is the heart of what the whole problem is trying to accomplish.

Suggested Questions Ask:

- *Are each of the divisions accurate?* (yes)

- *What labels will make the meaning of each answer clear?* ($7 \div 6$ is boxes divided by price, i.e., $\frac{7 \text{ boxes}}{6 \text{ dollars}}$, so the label for ≈ 1.17 is number of boxes per dollar. For $6 \div 7$ you have price divided by number of boxes, i.e., $\frac{6 \text{ boxes}}{7 \text{ dollars}}$, so the label is dollars per box.)

- *Which store offers the better deal?* (Using number of boxes per dollar, you are comparing 1.17 boxes per dollar for CornerMarket with 1.2 boxes per dollar for SuperFoodz. So SuperFoodz gives you more per dollar. You could also use dollars per box to answer the question.)

When the students seem ready, indicate that the problem on which they are to work has five parts, each of which asks for a comparison to be made that is easy to make with a unit rate.

   If your class period is too short for all five parts of the problem, have the students finish at home and summarize the next day.

   Let students work in small groups, but be sure each student understands each problem solution and makes a record of the solution.

Explore 3.4

As students are working, circulate and look for students who are able to articulate clearly what they are doing and why. These students can help in the summary.

Suggested Questions If students are having trouble, ask:

- *Why does dividing make sense here?* (Because you need to find what quantity of items are related to one unit of money, time, capacity, etc., so that you can make a comparison or description.)

- *How can you decide what the label for the answer to the division should be?* (By labeling the quantities in the division, you can see that the result of the division should be labeled as numerator label per unit of the denominator label. For example, 22 gal of gas to go 682 mi gives the unit rate $\frac{682 \text{ mi}}{22 \text{ gal}} = 31$ mi/gal. You can also write this relationship as $\frac{22 \text{ gal}}{682 \text{ mi}} \approx 0.0323$ gal/mi.)

- *How is labeling the quantities in the division helpful?* (The labeling keeps the order straight in deciding which quantity is the "per" quantity.)

Summarize 3.4

Call on students to give their answers and supporting arguments for each problem. Be sure to ask for alternative unit rates and labels for making comparisons as you discuss each problem.

Have some students write out models of the divisions with the quantity labels carried with the numerator and the denominator. Make the links to the numerator label and the denominator label in the label for the answer. The language of "per" helps some students get more comfortable with quantity *per* mile, *per* ounce, *per* minute, *per* day, etc.

3.4

What Does Dividing Tell You?

Mathematical Goal

- Confront the issue of what it means to divide in rate situations

Launch

Use the Getting Ready to engage students with the ideas.

Read through the situation and the questions, and give students a few minutes to think about the questions being asked. Ask:

- *Are each of the divisions accurate?*
- *What labels will make the meaning of each answer clear?*
- *Which store offers the better deal?*

Have students work in small groups.

If your class period is too short for all five parts of the problem, have the students finish at home and summarize the next day.

Materials

- Transparency 3.4A and 3.4B
- Transparency markers

Explore

As you circulate, look for students who are able to articulate clearly what they are doing and why.

If students are having trouble, ask:

- *Why does dividing make sense here?*
- *How can you decide what the label for the answer to the division should be?*
- *How is labeling the quantities in the division helpful?*

Materials

- Graphing calculators
- Grid paper

Summarize

Call on students to give their answers and supporting arguments for each problem.

Ask for alternative unit rates and labels for making comparisons as you discuss each problem.

Have some students write out models of the divisions with the quantity labels carried with the numerator and the denominator. Make the links to the numerator label and the denominator label in the label for the answer.

Materials

- Student notebooks

ACE Assignment Guide
for Problem 3.4

Differentiated
Instruction
Solutions for All Learners

Core 12

Other *Connections* 27–32; unassigned choices from previous problems

Adapted For suggestions about adapting ACE exercises, see the CMP *Special Needs Handbook*.

Connecting to Prior Units 32: *Stretching and Shrinking*

Answers to Problem 3.4

A. 1. $\frac{2 \text{ dollars}}{10 \text{ oranges}}$ = $0.20 per orange

2. $\frac{10 \text{ oranges}}{2 \text{ dollars}}$ = 5 oranges per dollar

3. See answers to 1 and 2.

4. (Figure 5)

B. 1. Miles per gallon or gallons per mile.

2. $\frac{682 \text{ miles}}{22 \text{ gallons}}$ = 31 mi/gal or

$\frac{22 \text{ gallons}}{682 \text{ miles}}$ ≈ 0.0323 gal/mi

3. Miles per gallon seems best because gas is purchased by the gallon and this tells you how far a tank will go. But either helps make comparisons.

C. 1. $\frac{100 \text{ maple trees}}{25 \text{ gallons of syrup}}$ = 4 trees per gallon of syrup

2. $\frac{25 \text{ gallons of syrup}}{100 \text{ maple trees}}$ = 0.25 gal per tree

D. 1. $\frac{18 \text{ gallons}}{5 \text{ minutes}}$ = 3.6 gal/min

2. $\frac{5 \text{ minutes}}{18 \text{ gallons}}$ ≈ 0.278 min/gal

E. 1. No.

2. By computing the price per can or the cans per dollar we can make a comparison. For CornerMarket we get about $1.13 per can or 0.89 cans per dollar. At CannedStuff we get about $0.83 per can or 1.2 cans per dollar. CannedStuff is a better deal.

Figure 5

Cost of Oranges at SuperFoodz

Number of Oranges	10	5	1	20	11	13
Cost	$2.00	$1.00	$0.20	$4.00	$2.20	$2.60

Comparing and Scaling Rates

The following examples illustrate situations involving another strategy to compare numbers.

- My mom's car gets 45 miles per gallon on the expressway.
- We need two sandwiches for each person at the picnic.
- I earn $3.50 per hour baby-sitting for my neighbor.
- The mystery meat label says 355 Calories per 6-ounce serving.
- My brother's top running rate is 8.5 kilometers per hour.

Each of these statements compares two different quantities. For example, one compares miles to gallons of gas. A comparison of two quantities measured in different units is a **rate.** You have used rates in earlier problems. For example, you used rates in finding pizza per person.

Getting Ready for Problem 3.1

- What two quantities are being compared in the rate statements above?
- Which of the rate statements is different from the others?

Notes _____

_____

_____

_____

Technology on Sale

Stores, catalogs, and Web sites often use rates in their ads. The ads sometimes give the cost for several items. You might see an offer like the one shown at the right.

Calculators for School

Fraction:	$120 for 20
Scientific:	$240 for 15
Graphing:	$800 for 10

The listed prices are for orders of 10, 15, or 20 calculators. But it's possible to figure the price for any number you want to purchase. One way to figure those prices is to build a *rate table*. A rate table is started below.

Price of Calculators for Schools

Number Purchased	1	2	3	4	5	10	15	20
Fraction Price	■	■	■	■	■	■	■	$120
Scientific Price	■	■	■	■	■	■	$240	■
Graphing Price	■	■	■	■	■	$800	■	■

Problem 3.1 Making and Using a Rate Table

Suppose you take orders over the phone for the calculator company. You should be quick with price quotes for orders of different sizes.

A. Build a rate table like the one above. Fill in prices for each type of calculator for orders of the sizes shown.

Use your rate table to answer Questions B–F.

B. How much does it cost to buy 53 fraction calculators? How much to buy 27 scientific calculators? How much to buy 9 graphing calculators?

C. How many fraction calculators can a school buy if it can spend $390? What if the school can spend only $84?

D. How many graphing calculators can a school buy if it can spend $2,500? What if the school can spend only $560?

E. What *arithmetic operation* (addition, subtraction, multiplication or division) do you use to find the cost per calculator?

F. Write an equation for each kind of calculator to show how to find the price for any number ordered.

ACE Homework starts on page 40.

34 Comparing and Scaling

Notes _____

_____

_____

_____

Sascha cycled on a route with different kinds of conditions. Sometimes he went uphill, sometimes he went mostly downhill. Sometimes he was on flat ground. He stopped three times to record his time and distance:

- Stop 1: 5 miles in 20 minutes
- Stop 2: 8 miles in 24 minutes
- Stop 3: 15 miles in 40 minutes

Problem 3.2 Finding Rates

Show your work. Label any rate that you find with appropriate units.

A. Find Sascha's rate in miles per hour for each part of the route.

B. 1. On which part was Sascha cycling fastest? On which part was he cycling slowest?

   2. How do your calculations in Question A support your answers?

C. Suppose you can maintain a steady rate of 13 miles per hour on a bike. How long will it take you to travel the same distance Sascha traveled in 1 hour and 24 minutes?

D. Suppose you were racing Sascha. What steady rate would you have to maintain to tie him?

ACE **Homework starts on page 40.**

Did You Know?

The highest rate ever recorded on a pedal-powered bicycle was 166.944 miles per hour. Fred Rompelberg performed this amazing feat on October 3, 1995, at the Bonneville Salt Flats in Utah. He was able to reach this rate by following a vehicle. The vehicle acted as a windshield for him and his bicycle.

Go Online
PHSchool.com **For:** Information about speed records **Web Code:** ane-9031

Investigation 3 Comparing and Scaling Rates **35**

STUDENT PAGE

STUDENT PAGE

Notes _____

_____

_____

_____

The ads below use rates to describe sale prices. To compare prices in sales such as these, it's often useful to find a unit rate. A **unit rate** is a rate in which one of the numbers being compared is 1 unit. The comparisons "45 miles per gallon," "$3.50 per hour," "8.5 kilometers per hour," and "two sandwiches for each person" are all unit rates. "Per gallon" means "for one gallon" and "per hour" means "for one hour."

Problem 3.3 Unit Rates and Equations

Use unit rates to compare the ad prices and to find the costs of various numbers of CDs at each store.

A. Which store has the lower price per CD?

B. For each store, write an equation (a rule) that you can use to calculate the cost c for any purchase of n compact discs.

C. Use the equations you just wrote for Question B. Write new equations to include 5% sales tax on any purchase.

Notes _____

_____

_____

_____

D. Suppose a Web site sells CDs for $8.99 per disc. There is no tax, but there is a shipping charge of $5 for any order. Write an equation to give the cost c of any order for n discs from the Web site.

E. Use your equations from Question C or make a rate table to answer each question.

1. How many discs do you have to order from the Web site to get a better deal than buying from Music City?

2. How many discs do you have to order from the Web site to get a better deal than buying from CD World?

ACE Homework starts on page 40.

3.4 What Does Dividing Tell You?

In this problem, the questions will help you decide which way to divide when you are finding a unit rate. The questions will also help you with the meaning of the quotient after you divide.

Getting Ready for Problem 3.4

Dario has two options for buying boxes of pasta. At CornerMarket he can buy seven boxes of pasta for $6. At SuperFoodz he can buy six boxes of pasta for $5.

At CornerMarket, he divided 7 by 6 and got 1.16666667. He then divided 6 by 7 and got 0.85714286. He was confused. What do these numbers tell about the price of boxes of pasta at CornerMarket?

Decide which makes more sense to you. Use that division strategy to compare the two store prices. Which store offers the better deal?

STUDENT PAGE

Notes _____

_____

_____

_____

Problem 3.4 Two Different Rates

Use division to find unit rates to solve the following questions. Label each unit rate.

A. SuperFoodz has oranges on sale at 10 for $2.

1. What is the cost per orange?

2. How many oranges can you buy for $1?

3. What division did you perform in each case? How did you decide what each division means?

4. Complete this rate table to show what you know.

Cost of Oranges at SuperFoodz						
Oranges	10	■	1	20	11	■
Cost	$2.00	$1.00	■	■	■	$2.60

B. Noralie used 22 gallons of gas to go 682 miles.

1. What are the two unit rates that she might compute?

2. Compute each unit rate and tell what it means.

3. Which seems more useful to you? Why?

38   Comparing and Scaling

STUDENT PAGE

Notes _____

_____

_____

_____

(38) 68

C. It takes 100 maple trees to make 25 gallons of maple syrup.

    1. How many maple trees does it take for 1 gallon of syrup?

    2. How much syrup can you get from one maple tree?

D. A 5-minute shower requires about 18 gallons of water.

    1. How much water per minute does a shower take?

    2. How long does a shower last if you use only 1 gallon of water?

E. 1. At the CornerMarket grocery store, you can buy eight cans of tomatoes for $9. The cans are the same size as those at CannedStuff, which sells six cans for $5. Are the tomatoes at CornerMarket a better buy than the tomatoes at CannedStuff?

    2. What comparison strategies did you use to choose between CornerMarket and CannedStuff tomatoes? Why?

ACE **Homework starts on page 40.**

Notes _____

_____

_____

_____

Applications

The problems that follow will give you practice in using rates (especially unit rates) in different situations. Be careful to use measurement units that match correctly in the rates you compute.

1. Maralah can drive her car 580 miles at a steady speed using 20 gallons of gasoline. Make a rate table showing the number of miles her car can be driven at this speed. Show 1, 2, 3, . . . , and 10 gallons of gas.

2. Joel can drive his car 450 miles at a steady speed using 15 gallons of gasoline. Make a rate table showing the number of miles his car can be driven at this speed. Show 1, 2, 3, . . . , and 10 gallons of gas.

3. Franky's Trail Mix Factory gives customers the following information. Use the pattern in the table to answer the questions.

Caloric Content of Franky's Trail Mix

Grams of Trail Mix	Calories
50	150
150	450
300	900
500	1,500

a. Fiona eats 75 grams of trail mix. How many Calories does she eat?

b. Rico eats trail mix containing 1,000 Calories. How many grams of trail mix does he eat?

c. Write an equation that you can use to find the number of Calories in any number of grams of trail mix.

d. Write an equation that you can use to find the number of grams of trail mix that will provide any given number of Calories.

Notes _____

_____

_____

_____

For Exercises 4–8, you will explore relationships among time, rate, and distance.

4. When she drives to work, Louise travels 10 miles in about 15 minutes. Kareem travels 23 miles in about 30 minutes. Who has the faster average speed?

5. Rolanda and Mali ride bikes at a steady pace. Rolanda rides 8 miles in 32 minutes. Mali rides 2 miles in 10 minutes. Who rides faster?

6. Fasiz and Dale drive at the same speed along a road. Fasiz drives 8 kilometers in 24 minutes. How far does Dale drive in 6 minutes?

7. On a long dirt road leading to camp, buses travel only 6 miles in 10 minutes.

    a. At this speed, how long does it take the buses to travel 18 miles?

    b. At this speed, how far do the buses go in 15 minutes?

8. **Multiple Choice** Choose the fastest walker.

    A. Montel walks 3 miles in 1 hour.

    B. Jerry walks 6 miles in 2 hours.

    C. Phil walks 6 miles in 1.5 hours.

    D. Rosie walks 9 miles in 2 hours.

9. The dairy store says it takes 50 pounds of milk to make 5 pounds of cheddar cheese.

    a. Make a rate table showing the amount of milk needed to make 5, 10, 15, 20, . . . , and 50 pounds of cheddar cheese.

    b. Make a coordinate graph showing the relationship between pounds of milk and pounds of cheddar cheese. First, decide which variable should go on each axis.

    c. Write an equation relating pounds of milk m to pounds of cheddar cheese c.

    d. Explain one advantage of each method (the graph, the table, and the equation) to express the relationship between milk and cheddar cheese production.

Investigation 3 Comparing and Scaling Rates   **41**

Notes

_____

_____

_____

_____

10. A dairy manager says it takes 70 pounds of milk to make 10 pounds of cottage cheese.

    a. Make a rate table for the amount of milk needed to make 10, 20, . . . , and 100 pounds of cottage cheese.

    b. Make a graph showing the relationship between pounds of milk and pounds of cottage cheese. First, decide which variable should go on each axis.

    c. Write an equation relating pounds of milk m to pounds of cottage cheese c.

    d. Compare the graph in part (b) to the graph in Exercise 9. Explain how they are alike and how they are different. What is the cause of the differences between the two graphs?

11. A store sells videotapes at $3.00 for a set of two tapes. You have $20. You can split a set and buy just one tape for the same price per tape as the set.

    a. How many tapes can you buy?

    b. Suppose there is a 7% sales tax on the tapes. How many can you buy? Justify your solution.

Homework Help Online
PHSchool.com
For: Help with Exercise 11
Web Code: ane-3311

12. Study the data in these rate situations. Then write the key relationship in three ways:

    • in fraction form with a label for each part
    • as two different unit rates with a label for each rate

    a. Latanya's 15-mile commute to work each day takes an average of 40 minutes.

    b. In a 5-minute test, one computer printer produced 90 pages of output.

    c. An advertisement for a Caribbean cruise trip promises 168 hours of fun for only $1,344.

    d. A long-distance telephone call lasts 20 minutes and costs $4.50.

Notes _____

_____

_____

_____

Connections

Rewrite each equation, replacing the variable with a number that makes a true statement.

13. $\frac{4}{9} \times n = 1\frac{1}{3}$

14. $n \times 2.25 = 90$

15. $n \div 15 = 120$

16. $180 \div n = 15$

17. Write two fractions with a product between 10 and 11.

18. Write two decimals with a product between 1 and 2.

A recent world-champion milk producer was a 4-year-old cow from Marathon, Wisconsin. The cow, Muranda Oscar Lucinda, produced a record 67,914 pounds of milk in one year! Use this information for Exercises 19–22.

19. Look back at your answers to Exercise 10. How much cottage cheese could be made from the amount of milk that Muranda Oscar Lucinda produced during her record year?

20. The average weight of a dairy cow is 1,500 pounds. How many dairy cows would be needed to equal the weight of the cottage cheese you found in Exercise 19?

21. One gallon of milk weighs about 8.7 pounds. Suppose a typical milk bucket holds about 3 gallons. About how many milk buckets would Muranda Oscar Lucinda's average daily production of milk fill?

22. One pound of milk fills about two glasses. About how many glasses of milk could you fill with Muranda Oscar Lucinda's average daily production of milk?

23. Some campers bike 10 miles for a nature study. Use this setting to write questions that can be answered by solving each equation. Find the answers, and explain what they tell about the bike ride.

a. $10 \div 8 = \blacksquare$ **b.** $1.2 \times \blacksquare = 10$ **c.** $\blacksquare \div 2 = 5$

Investigation 3 Comparing and Scaling Rates   **43**

Notes _____

_____

_____

_____

The table shows the mean times that students in one seventh-grade class spend on several activities during a weekend. The data are also displayed in the stacked bar graph below the table. Use both the table and the graph for Exercises 24 and 25.

Weekend Activities (hours)

Category	Boys	Girls	All Students
Sleeping	18.8	18.2	18.4
Eating	4.0	2.7	3.1
Recreation	7.8	6.9	7.2
Talking on the Phone	0.5	0.7	0.6
Watching TV	4.2	3.0	3.4
Doing Chores and Homework	3.6	5.8	5.1
Other	9.1	10.7	10.2

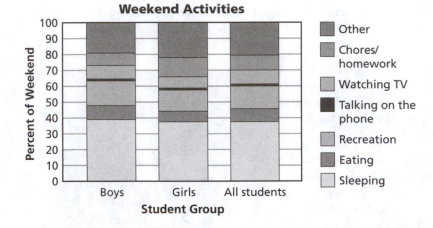

24. The stacked bar graph was made using the data from the table. Explain how it was constructed.

25. Suppose you are writing a report summarizing the class's data. You have space for either the table or the graph, but not both. What is one advantage of including the table? What is one advantage of including the stacked bar graph?

Notes
_____
_____
_____
_____

26. This table shows how to convert liters to quarts.

Liters	Quarts
1	1.06
4	4.24
5	5.30
9	9.54

  a. About how many liters are in 5.5 quarts?

  b. About how many quarts are in 5.5 liters?

  c. Write an equation for a rule that relates liters L to quarts Q.

Express each of the relationships in Exercises 27–31 as a unit rate. Label each unit rate with measurement units.

27. 12 cents for 20 beads

28. 8 cents for 10 nails

29. 405 miles on 15 gallons of gasoline

30. 3 cups of water for 2 cups of orange concentrate

31. $4 for 5 cans of soup

Go Online
PHSchool.com
For: Multiple-Choice Skills Practice
Web Code: ana-3354

32. The two clocks shown below are geometrically similar. One is a reduction of the other. Each outside edge of the larger clock is 2 centimeters long. Each outside edge of the smaller clock is 1.6 centimeters long.

  a. Write an equation relating the length L of any part of the large clock to the length S of the corresponding part of the small clock.

  b. Write an equation relating the area R of any part of the large clock to the area M of the corresponding part of the small clock.

  c. Write a decimal scale factor relating lengths in the large clock to lengths in the small clock. Explain how that scale factor is like a unit rate.

Notes _____

_____

_____

_____

Connections

STUDENT PAGE

Extensions

33. Chemistry students analyzed the contents of rust. They found that it is made up of iron and oxygen. Tests on samples of rust gave these data.

Contents of Rust

Amount of Rust (g)	Amount of Iron (g)	Amount of Oxygen (g)
50	35.0	15.0
100	70.0	30.0
135	94.5	40.5
150	105.0	45.0

   a. Suppose the students analyze 400 grams of rust. How much iron and how much oxygen should they find?

   b. Is the ratio of iron to oxygen the same in each sample? If so, what is it? If not, explain.

   c. Is the ratio of iron to total rust the same in each sample? If so, what is it? If not, explain.

34. A cider mill owner has pressed 240 liters of apple juice. He has many sizes of containers in which to pack the juice.

   a. The owner wants to package all the juice in containers of the same size. Copy and complete this table to show the number of containers of each size needed to hold the juice.

Containers Needed by Volume

Volume of Container (liters)	10	4	2	1	$\frac{1}{2}$	$\frac{1}{4}$	$\frac{1}{10}$
Number of Containers Needed	■	■	■	■	■	■	■

   b. Write an equation that relates the volume v of a container and the number n of containers needed to hold 240 liters of juice.

46   Comparing and Scaling

Notes
_____
_____
_____
_____

Mathematical Reflections 3

In this investigation, you learned to compare rates, to find unit rates, and to use rates to make tables and graphs and to write equations. The following questions will help you summarize what you have learned.

Think about your answers to these questions. Discuss your ideas with other students and your teacher. Then write a summary of your findings in your notebook.

The Picked Today fruit stand sells three green peppers for $1.50.

1. a. Describe the process for finding a unit rate for the peppers.

   b. Find two different unit rates to express the relationship between peppers and price. Explain what each unit rate tells.

   c. Fresh Veggie sells green peppers at five for $2.25. Compare Picked Today pepper prices with Fresh Veggie prices using two different kinds of unit rates.

   d. How do you decide whether the larger unit rate or the smaller unit rate is the better buy?

2. How would you construct a rate table for green pepper prices at the two vegetable stands? Explain what the entries in the table tell.

3. a. How would you write an equation to show the price for *n* peppers bought at Picked Today?

   b. Explain how the unit rate is used in writing the equation.

Notes _____

_____

_____

_____

Investigation 3

ACE Assignment Choices

Differentiated Instruction
Solutions for All Learners

Problem 3.1
Core 1–3, 33
Other *Connections* 13–18

Problem 3.2
Core 4–8
Other *Applications* 10; *Connections* 19–23; unassigned choices from previous problems

Problem 3.3
Core 9, 11
Other *Connections* 24–26, *Extensions* 34; unassigned choices from previous problems

Problem 3.4
Core 12
Other *Connections* 27–32; unassigned choices from previous problems

Adapted For suggestions about adapting Exercises 1, 2, and other ACE exercises, see the CMP *Special Needs Handbook*.
Connecting to Prior Units 13–18: *Bits and Pieces II, Bits and Pieces III*; 23: *Bits and Pieces II, Bits and Pieces III, Variables and Patterns*; 24, 25: *Data About Us*; 32: *Stretching and Shrinking*

Applications

1. Maralah's Driving Distance

Gallons	Miles Driven
1	29
2	58
3	87
4	116
5	145
6	174
7	203
8	232
9	261
10	290

2. Joel's Driving Distance

Gallons	Miles Driven
1	30
2	60
3	90
4	120
5	150
6	180
7	210
8	240
9	270
10	300

3. a. 225 Calories. Since 150 g of trail mix contains 450 Calories, an equivalent ratio of grams to Calories is 1 : 3. From this scaled-down ratio, you can scale up to 75 : 225, which means that 75 g of trail mix would contain 225 Calories.

b. 333.33 . . . ($\approx$ 333). The ratio of Calories to grams is 3 to 1. 1,000 : 333.33 . . . is equivalent. Or, 1,000 Calories is $\frac{2}{3}$ of 1,500 Calories, so Freddy ate $\frac{2}{3}$ of 500 g, or about 333 g.

c. Number of Calories = 3 × number of grams ($C = 3g$)

d. Number of grams = number of Calories ÷ 3 ($g = C \div 3$, or $g = C \times \frac{1}{3}$)

4. Kareem is faster. He travels 23 mi ÷ 30 min ≈ 0.77 mi/min while Louise travels 10 mi ÷ 15 min ≈ 0.67 mi/min.

5. Rolanda rides faster. She travels 8 mi ÷ 32 min = 0.25 mi/min while Mali travels 2 mi ÷ 10 min = 0.2 mi/min.

6. Dale drives 2 km in 6 min. If you use equivalent ratios 8 : 24 = ■ : 6, then ■ = 2.

7. **a.** The bus would take 30 min to travel 18 mi. 6 mi/10 min = 18 mi/■ min. Using a scale factor of 3, ■ = 10 × 3, or 30 min.

   b. In 15 min, the bus would go 1.5 × 6 = 9 mi.

8. D

9. **a.** **Milk Needed to Make Cheddar Cheese**

Cheese (lb)	Milk (lb)
5	50
10	100
15	150
20	200
25	250
30	300
35	350
40	400
45	450
50	500

b. **Cheddar Cheese Production from Milk**

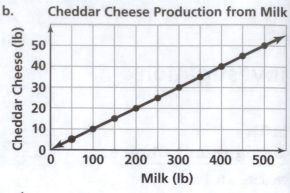

c. $\frac{1}{10} m = c$, or $m = 10c$

d. Possible answers: The graph visually shows the relationship between amounts of milk and cheese. The table allows one to look up how much milk is needed to yield any given cheese amount. The equation allows for quick calculation of the amount of milk needed for any amount of cheese.

10. **a.** **Milk Needed to Make Cottage Cheese**

Cheese (lb)	Milk (lb)
10	70
20	140
30	210
40	280
50	350
60	420
70	490
80	560
90	630
100	700

b. (Figure 6)

Figure 6

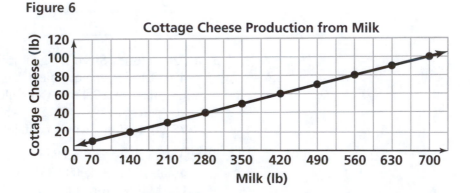

Cottage Cheese Production from Milk

c. $\frac{1}{7}m = c$, or $m = 7c$

d. Possible answer: Both graphs are straight lines and cross at the point $(0, 0)$. The cottage cheese graph is steeper than the cheddar cheese graph, because cheddar cheese requires more milk per pound than cottage cheese.

11. a. Each tape costs $3.00 \div 2 = \$1.50$. With $20, you can buy $20.00 \div 1.50 = 13.33 \ldots$ tapes, or 13 tapes with $0.50 remaining.

b. Possible answers: On 13 tapes, the sales tax would be $\$19.50 \times 0.07 = \$1.365$ or $1.37. You would not have enough to pay the sales tax. If you bought 12 tapes, the sales tax would be $\$18.00 \times 0.07 = \$1.26$. The total cost would be $\$18.00 + 1.26 = \$19.26$. Or, since each tape has a sales tax of $\$1.50 \times 0.07 = 10.5$ cents, each tape costs $1.605, so you can buy $\$20.00 \div \$1.605 \approx 12$ tapes. Therefore, at most you could buy 12 tapes.

12. a. (1) 40 min to go 15 mi $= \frac{40 \text{ min}}{15 \text{ mi}}$

(2) 40 min/15 mi ≈ 2.7 min per mi

(3) 15mi/40 min $= 0.375$ mi per min

b. (1) 90 pages in 5 min $= \frac{90 \text{ pages}}{5 \text{ min}}$

(2) 90 pages/5 min $= 18$ pages per min

(3) 5 min/90 pages ≈ 0.06 min per page

c. (1) $1,344 for 168 h $= \frac{\$1,344}{168 \text{ h}}$

(2) $1,344/168 h $= \$8$ per h

(3) 168 h/$1,344 $= 0.125$ h per dollar

d. (1) $4.50 in 20 min $= \frac{\$4.50}{20 \text{ min}}$

(2) $4.50/20 min $= \$0.225$ ($0.23) per min

(3) 20 min/$4.50 ≈ 4.4 min per dollar

For the Teacher It is possible to express each ratio or unit rate in different ways, such as minutes per dollar or dollars per minute. Ask your students which way makes the most sense to them. Then ask what type of information each way gives.

Connections

13. $\left(\frac{4}{9}\right) \times 3 = 1\frac{1}{3}$ **14.** $40 \times 2.25 = 90$

15. $1,800 \div 15 = 120$ **16.** $180 \div 12 = 15$

17. Possible answer: $\frac{5}{2} \times \frac{21}{5} = 10.5$

18. Possible answers: $2.1 \times 0.9 = 1.89$; or $5.5 \times 0.25 = 1.375$

19. Since 7 lb of milk will make 1 lb of cottage cheese, $67,914 \div 7 =$ about 9,702 lb of cottage cheese could be produced from that amount of milk.

20. Since $9,702 \div 1,500 = 6.468$, it would take more than 6 cows to balance this quantity of cottage cheese.

21. One milk bucket holds $3 \times 8.7 = 26.1$ lb of milk. Muranda Oscar Lucinda produced about $67,914 \div 365 \approx 186.1$ lb of milk per day, or about $186.1 \div 26.1 \approx 7.13$ buckets of milk per day.

22. about $186.1 \times 2 = 372.2$ glasses of milk per day

23. a. If the campers biked for 10 mi traveling 8 mi/h, how many hours did they ride? The campers biked for 1.25 h. It tells how long they biked.

b. If the campers biked for 1.2 h, what would their speed per hour be in order to bike 10 mi? The average biking speed is $8\frac{1}{3}$ mi/h. It gives their biking rate in miles per hour.

c. How many miles did the campers bike if they broke their bike ride into two parts and biked 5 mi during each part? 10 mi.

24. Percents were calculated for boys, girls, and all students in each category. Then the percents were stacked on top of each other in the same order to show the whole 100%.

25. The table makes it easy to compare exact hours spent on each activity. The bar graph is a quick, visual way of comparing the percentage of time spent in each category by each group. Also, comparing the heights of corresponding bands is a quick way to compare the percentage of time spent in each category between the different groups.

26. a. There are $1 \div 1.06 \approx 0.94$ L per quart, so 5.5 qt is $5.5 \times 0.94 \approx 5.17$ L.

b. In 5.5 L there are $5.5 \times 1.06 = 5.83$ quarts.

c. From the unit rates, $Q = 1.06L$ and $L = 0.94Q$.

27. Unit rate: 0.6 cent per bead

28. Unit rate: 0.8 cent per nail

29. Unit rate: 27 mi/gal

30. Unit rate: 1.5 c of water per cup of concentrate

31. Unit price: $0.80 per can of soup

32. a. $L = 1.25S$ ($L = \frac{5}{4}S$)

   b. $R = (\frac{5}{4})^2 \times M$ or $[R = (1.25)^2 \times M]$

   c. 1.25. The scale factor is like a unit rate because they both are what you can multiply the original by to get the new number (measurement, etc.). While the scale factor is 1.25, it could also be thought of as 1.25 units of length of the large clock to 1 unit of length of the small clock.

   For the Teacher Discuss how students derived the answer to 32(b). What steps were in their thinking process and what methods did they use to go about solving the problem?

Extensions

33. a. 280 g of iron and 120 g of oxygen. The fraction of oxygen to rust is $0.3(\frac{3}{10})$. The fraction of iron to rust is $0.7(\frac{7}{10})$.

   b. Yes. 7 : 3

   c. Yes. 7 : 10

34. a. (Figure 7)

   b. *Number needed = 240 ÷ Volume*, or $n = \frac{240}{v}$

Possible Answers to Mathematical Reflections

1. a. You divide one quantity by another quantity and label the answer appropriately. If you divide miles by hours, you get miles per hour. If you divide numbers of peppers by cost, you get peppers per dollar. If you divide dollars by peppers, you get cost per pepper.

   b. Peppers per dollar—gives the number of peppers one can buy per dollar (2 peppers per $1). Cost per pepper gives the amount a single pepper costs ($0.50 per pepper).

   c. For Fresh Veggies, you can say that 5 divided by 2.25 gives 2.22 . . . , but what does the quotient mean? It means 2.22 . . . peppers per dollar. But 2.25 divided by 5 gives 0.45 as the cost per pepper. Compare these with $3 ÷ 1.5 = 2$ peppers per dollar and $1.5 ÷ 3 = 0.5$ per pepper.

   d. Each comparison shows that Fresh Veggies is a better deal. For peppers per dollar, the greater unit rate is better. For cost per pepper, the better deal is the smaller unit rate.

2. Create a table with two rows, one for each kind of related quantity, price of peppers from Picked Today and price of peppers from Fresh Veggie. For example, with 3 for $1.50, under the "3" column, one row would be peppers with a price of $1.50. You could write a variety of different pepper amounts, such as 1–10, 15, 20, 30, and so on, across the columns and then determine the prices that correspond to each amount of peppers. The entries tell the amount of each variable or unit given a set amount of the other kind of quantity or measure.

3. a. 3 peppers for $1.50 means that the unit rate is 50 cents per pepper. The equation is $p = 0.50n$.

   b. In an equation, unit rates are the number used to multiply the amount of units in order to find a total. (This number is called the coefficient. Some students might say it is the number next to the variable, or the number that you multiply the variable by). In the equation: price $= 0.50n$, 50 cents is multiplied by the number of peppers to find the total price for n peppers.

Figure 7

Containers Needed by Volume

Volume of Containers (liters)	10	4	2	1	$\frac{1}{2}$	$\frac{1}{4}$	$\frac{1}{10}$
Number of Containers Needed	24	60	120	240	480	960	2,400

Investigation 4 — Making Sense of Proportions

Mathematical and Problem-Solving Goals

- Apply proportional reasoning to solve for the unknown part when one part of two equal ratios is unknown

- Set up and solve proportions that arise in applications

- Use ratios and scaling up or scaling down (finding equivalent ratios) to find the missing value in a proportion

- Develop insight and flexibility in choosing strategies for solving problems requiring proportional reasoning

Summary of Problems

Problem 4.1 Setting Up and Solving Proportions

Students are introduced to proportions as setting two equivalent ratios equal. They learn to write four versions of a proportion and to solve proportions to find a missing value.

Problem 4.2 Everyday Use of Proportions

Students practice what they have learned about setting up and solving proportions to solve several problems in context where the numbers are relatively simple.

Problem 4.3 Developing Strategies for Solving Proportions

Students analyze proportional thinking and solidify this method of finding a missing part of an equivalent ratio.

	Suggested Pacing	Materials for Students	Materials for Teachers	ACE Assignments
All	$4\frac{1}{2}$ days	Graphing calculators, blank transparencies and markers or chart paper and markers (optional), student notebooks	Transparency markers	
4.1	2 days		Transparencies 4.1A and 4.1B	1, 2, 15–17, 21–23
4.2	1 day			3–5, 18–20, 25, 26
4.3	1 day	Labsheets 4ACE Exercise 27a and 4ACE Exercise 27b		6–14, 24, 27, 28
MR	$\frac{1}{2}$ day			

Goals

- Apply proportional reasoning to solve for the unknown part when one part of two equal ratios is unknown

- Set up and solve proportions that arise in applications

To help students understand the context of the problem, go over the introductory page of the investigation. The four situations in the introduction represent the kinds of situations students will encounter in the investigation. Have students suggest strategies for each one of the four situations. Then transition into the Launch of Problem 4.1.

This problem is designed to focus students' attention on setting ratios equal to form proportions. If a quantity is unknown in one of the ratios, this is a general strategy that often makes the work simpler. The solution to a proportion can be found by using what students know about finding equivalent fractions to scale proportions up or down so that denominators (or numerators) are equal and the solution can be read from the scaled ratio. They can also be solved in other ways such as finding unit rates.

The students by now have several ways to reason about a proportion situation: rate tables, scaling, and unit rates. As you work through the problems in this investigation, encourage students to set up and solve proportions, but be sure to look at several solution strategies as you discuss the problems.

Launch 4.1

Take time to discuss the introductory material carefully. Use the *polygon scaling* situation to give students a chance to try out the ideas before moving into Problem 4.1.

- *Now that we have looked at some ways of setting up proportions, let's look together at the polygon-scaling problem in the Getting Ready. The question we need to solve is: How long is the corresponding side in the similar figure?* (Read the text with the students.)

Suggested Questions

- *The scale factor is given as 2. If you have a measure of a length on the smaller polygon, how do you use the scale factor to find the corresponding length on the larger figure?* (You multiply the length by the scale factor, 2)

- *We know the length of a side on the larger figure. Will the corresponding length on the smaller figure be larger or smaller?* (Smaller.)

- *What is the ratio between lengths in the two similar figures?* (The ratio between the two would be 2 to 1 or 1 to 2 depending on whether you are going from large to small or small to large.)

- *Now I want each of you to write a proportion that relates the two ratios in the problem and solve the proportion.* (Possible answers: $\frac{2}{1} = \frac{10\,\text{cm}}{x\,\text{cm}}$, $\frac{1}{x\,\text{cm}} = \frac{2}{10\,\text{cm}}$, $\frac{1}{2} = \frac{x\,\text{cm}}{10\,\text{cm}}$, $\frac{x\,\text{cm}}{1} = \frac{10\,\text{cm}}{2}$; $x = 5$)

- *What is the length of the corresponding side in the smaller figure?* (5 centimeters)

- *Let's collect each different kind of ratio you wrote and keep them posted on the board while you use similar strategies to work on Problem 4.1.* (Be sure to have each of four versions of a proportion relating 2 to 1 and 10 to x.)

Read Question A together so that the class sees that the two students in the problem have found a solution to a proportion, but reasoned in different ways. The goal here is for students to see this is where proportions are especially efficient. Remind them that a proportion is just an equation that sets two ratios equal.

After you feel comfortable that the students are ready to try the problem, use a Think-Pair-Share arrangement. This allows students to try out their ideas alone and then with a partner. After all pairs have made progress, a discussion and comparison of strategies between two pairs is a good preparation for the summary.

Assign Question A to be done in class. Follow that with a summary. Assign Questions B–D after the summary or for homework. Be sure to talk about these parts the next day.

Explore 4.1

During the Question A exploration, focus your questions to groups on explaining the thinking of the two students whose work is given. Both Adrianna and Joey are using what they know about equivalent fractions to reason with proportions.

For Questions B and C, encourage students to write proportions, but allow them to use strategies that make sense to them to solve the problems. As you circulate, ask students to find a second way of thinking that will solve the problem. This can build flexibility in proportion solving that makes problems with nice numbers very easy to solve.

Note: If the numbers are not so nice, then an algorithm for solving proportions is very useful. We return to proportion solving early in grade eight and develop a general method for solving proportions as a part of equation solving.

If students are struggling on Question D, remind them that they studied situations like these in a geometry context in *Stretching and Shrinking*. Draw a picture of two similar triangles and label the values of two corresponding parts. Then give the value in the first triangle for another pair of corresponding parts and ask students to find the value of the corresponding part.

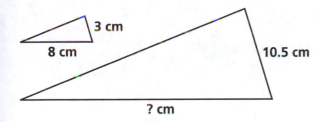

Suggested Question

- *If you know two shapes are similar, how do you use that information to find the values of two sets of corresponding parts when the value of one is missing?*

Summarize 4.1

Go over each part of Question A asking groups to share their solutions and their strategies. If you assign Questions B–D for homework, try to get the summary of Question A done in class before the homework.

Go over Questions B–D the next day. In Question B especially, focus on clear explanations for an algorithm (procedure) for solving a proportion for a missing quantity. Help students see that their knowledge of how to find equivalent fractions, unit rates, and building rate tables is very helpful here.

Question D relates to *Stretching and Shrinking* and is an important connection for making sense of solving proportions. You may wish to use Transparency 4.1B.

Setting Up and Solving Proportions

Mathematical Goals

- Apply proportional reasoning to solve for the unknown part when one part of two equal ratios is unknown
- Set up and solve proportions that arise in applications

Launch

Take time to discuss the introductory material carefully. Use the *polygon scaling* situation to give students a chance to try out the ideas before moving into Problem 4.1.

Ask:

- *The scale factor is given as 2. If you have a measure of a length on the smaller polygon, how do you use the scale factor to find the corresponding length on the larger figure?*
- *We know the length of a side on the larger figure. Will the corresponding length on the smaller figure be larger or smaller?*
- *What is the ratio between lengths in the two similar figures?*
- *Now I want each of you to write a proportion that relates the two ratios in the problem and solve the proportion.*
- *What is the length of the corresponding side in the smaller figure?*

Use a Think-Pair-Share arrangement.

If time is an issue, just assign Question A to be done in class. Follow that with a summary and assign Questions B–D for homework.

Materials
- Transparencies 4.1A, 4.1B

Vocabulary
- proportion

Explore

If students are struggling, remind them that they studied situations like these in a geometry context in *Stretching and Shrinking*. Draw a picture of two similar triangles and label the values of two corresponding parts. Then give the value in the first triangle for another pair of corresponding parts and ask students to find the value of the corresponding part.

- *If you know two shapes are similar, how do you use that information to find the values of two sets of corresponding parts when the value of one is missing?*

Materials
- Graphing calculators

Summarize

Go over each part of Question A. Ask groups to share their solutions and their strategies.

In Question B especially, focus on clear explanations for an algorithm (procedure) for solving a proportion for a missing quantity. Help students see that their knowledge of how to find equivalent fractions is very helpful here.

Materials
- Transparency 4.1B
- Student notebooks

continued on next page

Question D relates to *Stretching and Shrinking* and is an important connection for making sense of solving proportions.

ACE Assignment Guide for Problem 4.1

Differentiated Instruction
Solutions for All Learners

Core 1, 2, 15–17
Other *Connections* 21–23

Adapted For suggestions about adapting Exercise 2 and other ACE exercises, see the CMP *Special Needs Handbook*.
Connecting to Prior Units 21–23: *Stretching and Shrinking*

Answers to Problem 4.1

A. 1. Because $\frac{20}{20}$ is equal to 1 and multiplying any ratio by a fraction equal to one creates an equivalent ratio. Adrianna chose $\frac{20}{20}$ to represent 1 because 20 is the factor that you would multiply by 9 to get 180.

2. The denominators are equivalent because the ratios and numerators are equivalent.

3. Yes, because Adrianna found equivalent ratios by finding equivalent numerators. She did this by scaling up the original ratio of 9 dogs to 8 cats using 20 as the scale factor.

4. Joey found equivalent ratios by finding equivalent denominators. He scaled up by 10 and found a ratio equivalent to the original. Then he doubled that ratio producing another ratio equivalent to the first.

5. Because Joey scaled up to find equivalent denominators, the numerators became equivalent.

B. 1. 25 calculators. $\frac{20 \text{ calculators}}{\$1{,}000} = \frac{x \text{ calculators}}{\$1{,}250}$. The scale factor is 1.25 and $20 \times 1.25 = 25$.

2. 2,120. $\frac{20}{100} = \frac{x}{10{,}600}$. The scale factor is 106. $106 \times 20 = 2{,}120$.

C. 1. 20. The scale factor is 4, and $4 \times 5 = 20$. $\frac{8}{5} = \frac{32}{x}$ and $\frac{8 \times 4}{5 \times 4} = \frac{32}{20}$

2. 5.25. The scale factor is 0.75, and $7 \times 0.75 = 5.25$. $\frac{7}{12} = \frac{x}{9}$ and $\frac{7 \times 0.75}{12 \times 0.75} = \frac{5.25}{9}$

3. 35. The scale factor is 5, and $5 \times 7 = 35$. $\frac{25}{x} = \frac{5}{7}$ and $\frac{5 \times 5}{7 \times 5} = \frac{25}{35}$

4. $\frac{8}{3}$. The scale factor is $\frac{1}{3}$, and $\frac{1}{3} \times 8 = \frac{8}{3}$.

$$\frac{x}{3} = \frac{8}{9} \text{ and } \frac{8 \times \frac{1}{3}}{9 \times \frac{1}{3}} = \frac{\frac{8}{3}}{3}$$

Solving proportions can be done by determining the scale factor between the two numerators or denominators, depending on where the number you are trying to solve for (x) is located. In $\frac{3}{5} = \frac{9}{x}$, divide 3 into 9 to find that the scale factor is 3. Then multiply 5 by the scale factor (3), which will solve for x and in essence give you equivalent fractions. It is important to find the common factor or scale factor to multiply both numerator and denominator by to achieve equivalency. Students will have other ways to solve these problems all of which likely involve a version of such thinking: rate tables, unit rates, and scale factors have similarities.

D. 1. One possible proportion is:

$$\frac{x}{3.5} = \frac{5.2}{4.6} \text{ and } \frac{5.2 \times 0.76}{4.6 \times 0.76} \approx \frac{3.96}{3.5} \rightarrow x \approx 3.96$$

$$\frac{y}{5} = \frac{4.6}{5.2} \text{ and } \frac{4.6 \times 0.96}{5.2 \times 0.96} \approx \frac{4.42}{5} \rightarrow y \approx 4.42$$

2. $\frac{h}{5} = \frac{48}{8}$ and $\frac{4.8 \times 0.625}{8 \times 0.625} = \frac{30}{5} \rightarrow h = 30$ ft

4.2 Everyday Use of Proportions

Goals

- Set up and solve proportions that arise in applications

- Use ratios and scaling up or scaling down (finding equivalent ratios) to find the missing value in a proportion

In this problem a set of comparisons in everyday situations is given. The numbers are relatively simple. This provides the students practice with solving proportions and looking at how these methods compare to other ways of solving such problems.

Launch 4.2

Suggested Questions Ask:

- *Some of the problems you will solve today are statements that are used in everyday situations to make quick estimates about needed quantities.*

- *Have you ever heard of a "rule of thumb"?* (Some of the students may have some interesting examples. Some may use rules of thumb in sports. Offer the rule of thumb, "A yard is the distance from my nose to my fingertip when my arm is outstretched.")

- *What does your rule of thumb mean and how might it be helpful?* (This rule of thumb is often used by seamstresses to measure material. Make the connection to benchmarks: rules of thumb like this one allow us to estimate common quantities quickly.)

- *In your work today you will see some problems that involve rules of thumb and some that are familiar situations.*

Display or read each problem, and verify that the class understands what each is saying. Then move the class into the exploration.

Let the class do this in pairs (or groups if you are confident that each student is actively engaged in the thinking process.) You might have each student think about the first problem and then move them into pairs (or groups) to discuss their strategies.

Explore 4.2

Students may need to be reminded to be careful of the units or labels for the quantities they are dealing with.

- *When you were finding ratios, rates, and unit rates in earlier problems, you had to be careful about the measurement units and labels for the quantities. Why?* [Because the labels give meaning to the numbers. They help you know what the result of a division (or another operation) means.]

- *Be sure to include measurement labels for each quantity in each step of your work.*

Look for the different ways that students are thinking about the problem. Make sure that these strategies get discussed in the summary.

Summarize 4.2

Suggested Questions Ask:

- *I need a volunteer to give the answer to Question A and to explain how you found the answer and why it makes sense.* (Repeat for all problems.)

- *Does someone in another group want to challenge this solution or offer another solution strategy?*

If this takes too long, wait until the solutions to all of the problems have been given and then reflect on the different strategies. Some students may comment that they prefer the way another group thought about the problem. If so, ask why— it may have been shorter, more efficient, more general, etc. Select different groups to represent different strategies that you observed during the exploration.

- *If you had to solve a problem such as the ones in Problem 4.2 now, what solution strategy would you use and why?*

Everyday Use of Proportions

Mathematical Goals

- Set up and solve proportions that arise in applications
- Use ratios and scaling up or scaling down (finding equivalent ratios) to find the missing value in a proportion

Launch

- *Have you ever heard of a "rule of thumb"?*
- *What does your rule of thumb mean and how it might be helpful?*

If necessary, offer the rule of thumb, "A yard is the distance from my nose to my fingertip when my arm is outstretched."

Display or read each rule of thumb in the problem, and verify that the class understands what each is saying. Then move the class into the exploration.

Have students work in pairs or groups.

Materials
- Blank transparencies
- Transparency markers

Explore

Students may need to be reminded to be careful of the units or labels for the quantities they are dealing with.

- *When you were finding ratios, rates, and unit rates in earlier problems, you had to be careful about the measurement units and labels for the quantities. Why?*

Materials
- Graphing calculators

Summarize

- *I need a volunteer to give the answer to Question A and to explain how you found the answer and why it makes sense. (Repeat for all problems.)*
- *Does someone in another group want to challenge this solution or offer another solution strategy?*

If this takes too long, wait until the solutions to all of the problems have been given and then reflect on the different strategies.

Consider asking:

- *If you had to solve a problem such as the ones in Problem 4.2 now, what solution strategy would you use and why?*

Materials
- Student notebooks

ACE Assignment Guide
for Problem 4.2

Differentiated Instruction
Solutions for All Learners

Core 3–5, 25, 26
Other *Connections* 18–20; unassigned choices from previous problems

Adapted For suggestions about adapting ACE exercises, see the CMP *Special Needs Handbook*.
Connecting to Prior Units 18: *Variables and Patterns*; 19, 20: *How Likely Is It?, Bits and Pieces III*

Answers to Problem 4.2

A. Using a unit rate of 0.01 miles per Calorie, we can multiply the $1,200 \times 0.01$ to get 12 miles. Or, since $500 \times 2.4 = 1,200, 5 \times 2.4 = 12$.
$\frac{5 \text{ miles}}{500 \text{ Calories}} = \frac{? \text{ miles}}{1,200 \text{ Calories}}$ to get $\frac{12 \text{ miles}}{1,200 \text{ Calories}}$.
Some students may do a unit rate idea with this thinking: 5 miles for 500 Calories = 1 mile for 100 Calories. So, 12 miles for 1,200 Calories. Some students might use a rate table to keep track of their thinking:

Calories Burned While Jogging

Miles	5	1	12
Calories	500	100	1,200

B. 3 hours. The ratio of 8 to 12 is the same as 2 to 3. This ratio scaling also tells you that 3 hours is the solution. You could also compute a unit rate of 4 miles per hour and multiply by 3 to get 12 miles in 3 hours.

C. 1. Possible answer: Taking the time to do a job right saves you more time later on.

  2. 225 stitches saved. The ratio is 1 taken to 9 saved. 25 taken would give 9×25 saved.

D. $\frac{2 \text{ tsp}}{20 \text{ lb}} = \frac{? \text{ tsp}}{75 \text{ lb}} = \frac{2 \times 3.75 \text{ tsp}}{20 \times 3.75 \text{ lb}} = \frac{7.5 \text{ tsp}}{75 \text{ lb}}$, so Bruiser gets 7.5 teaspoons. By the same kind of reasoning Dust Ball gets $0.35 \times 2 \text{ tsp} = 0.7$ teaspoons of vitamins.

E. $s = \frac{1}{1.8} \times 12$ cm; $s = 6\frac{2}{3}$ cm, or ≈ 6.67 cm

Mathematics Background
For background on cross-multiplying, see page 7.

Goal

- Develop insight and flexibility in choosing strategies for solving problems requiring proportional reasoning

The temptation is just to show students cross-multiplication. However, taking a sensible approach gives students the opportunity to develop flexibility in solving proportional reasoning problems so that a chosen technique fits the situation and often supports additional insight into the problem. We do want students to have efficient ways of solving such problems, but to arrive at these in such a way that the student knows not just how but why a procedure works. We return to general proportion solving in grade eight and develop a general algorithm.

Launch 4.3

Suggested Questions Ask:

- *Who can tell us a situation that this proportion, $\frac{3}{5} = \frac{x}{20}$, might represent?* (It could be a recipe that calls for 3 cups of couscous to serve 5 people and you need to serve 20 people. How much couscous do you need? Or it could be 3 hours to write 5 pages of text on a book report but the teacher wants 20 pages! How long will it take to type? There are many other possibilities.)

- *So, how can we solve this proportion?* (Various ways. Be sure that this summary of ways reviews what students have developed in 4.2.)

- *For $\frac{3}{5} = \frac{x}{20}$, how would you find a scaling factor to make the denominator the same?* (You need to multiply the numerator and the denominator by a quantity that will scale the ratio $\frac{3}{5}$ so that its denominator is 20. To find the scaling factor, we divide the denominator of the ratio with the unknown in its numerator by the denominator of the other ratio. This is $\frac{20}{5}$ which equals 4.)

- *So, what do we do with the 4?* (We use it to write an equivalent ratio (fraction) for the ratio $\frac{3}{5}$ that has 20 in the denominator. This gives $\frac{12}{20}$ and tells us that $x = 12$ because if the denominators of two equivalent ratios are the same, then the numerators must be the same.)

- *So, if you apply these ideas to the proportion $\frac{3}{4} = \frac{x}{6}$, how do you solve it?* (Well, you would find $6 \div 4$ to get the scaling factor and multiply this scaling number by the numerator and the denominator of the ratio $\frac{3}{4}$ so that it will have a denominator of 6. So, $6 \div 4 = 1\frac{1}{2}$ and $\frac{3 \times 1.5}{4 \times 1.5} = \frac{4.5}{6}$ so $x = 4.5$ or $4\frac{1}{2}$.)

- *Can you build a rate table to help solve this proportion?* (Yes. The table might include the following:)

Numerator	3	6	12
Denominator	5	10	20

- *Can you find a unit rate to help solve this proportion?* (Yes. $3 \div 5 = 0.6$ and $0.6 \times 20 = 12$.)

These are the kinds of ideas that you will be using to solve Problem 4.3. You are asked to set up a proportion, but then you may choose a strategy for solving that makes sense to you. Practice more than one kind of strategy as you proceed through the problems.

Have students work in groups of two or three. Be sure that each student is working each problem and making a record of how the solutions were obtained.

INVESTIGATION 4

Notice that all parts of the problem require students to write or at least to solve problems stated as a proportion. While many students will have more informal means to solve these problems, it is important that they see how their own ideas are useful in solving proportions. Their own methods are related to systematic proportion solving and taking the time to help students see the more systematic underpinning of their ideas makes it possible for students to solve more difficult proportions. Continually ask students to articulate their strategy into a set of steps that can be used to solve another proportional problem.

As you circulate look for student ideas that need to be shared in the summary. Also look for student misconceptions that need to surface and be discussed in the summary.

Suggested Questions If students are having difficulty deciding how to find the scaling number in a situation such as Question B, ask:

- *In Question B, we have to solve the proportion $\frac{705}{3} = \frac{x}{240}$. Is the scaling factor for the ratios greater than or less than 1?* (Larger than 1 because we need to scale 3 up to 240.)

- *So what division will give us the scaling factor?* ($240 \div 3 = 80$. This is greater than 1 and will scale the number 3 up to 240 and 705 up to 56,400.)

- *What is the unit rate for Question B, $\frac{705}{3} = \frac{x}{240}$?* (Since we know the number of enchiladas and need the Calories, we need the Calories per enchilada, which is 235. Then we can multiply 240×235 to get the total Calories—56,400.)

- *Let's see. Using scaling we divided 240 by 3 and then multiplied by 705. So the arithmetic looked like this: $\frac{240}{3} \times 705$. In the unit rate approach what did the arithmetic look like?* ($\frac{705}{3} \times 240$)

- *Are these the same?* (Yes, because you have $(240 \times 705) \div 3$ in each case!)

We found that $\frac{705}{3} = \frac{x}{240}$ is the same as $\frac{705}{3} \times 240 = x$. As you solve other proportions, ask yourself whether this always works for x in the numerator problems.

Suggested Questions

- *Who can give me a proportion for the jet descending altitude?* (Collect as many different proportions as the students have written and list these on the board, chart paper, or the overhead. $\frac{10}{4,000} = \frac{x}{5,280}$; $\frac{4000}{10} = \frac{5,280}{x}$; $\frac{10}{x} = \frac{4,000}{5,280}$; $\frac{x}{10} = \frac{5,280}{4,000}$)

- *Now I need some examples of solution strategies.* (For $\frac{10}{4,000} = \frac{x}{5,280}$, the scaling factor is $\frac{5,280}{4,000} = 1.32$. So we have $\frac{10 \times 1.32}{4,000 \times 1.32} = \frac{13.2}{5,280} \rightarrow x = 13.2$. Students may want to present solutions to other forms of the proportion.)

Be sure to look back and compare the solution. You want students to begin to develop a procedure that will make for efficiency in solving proportions, but do not want to force the issue too far too soon as it will turn off students' thinking and turn on memorization.

You can continue to ask students to record the arithmetic involved in solving a proportion by two different methods as illustrated in the Explore. Noticing that you do the same computations in possibly a different order helps move students confidently toward more systematic solution strategies.

Discuss the other parts of the problem in similar ways. Give special attention to Question D where students are forced to deal with the unknown in the denominator. Here you want to get the numerators to be the same so that the denominators are the same and you can read off the value of x. By this time some students may see that inverting each of the fractions keeps equality. For example, students know that $\frac{2}{3} = \frac{4}{6}$. The question is, does $\frac{3}{2} = \frac{6}{4}$? The answer is yes.

For the Teacher If you have a class that understands and catches on easily to solving proportions, you might want to go a step further to look at a general strategy for proportion solving. If you choose to do so, the following shows that same kind of thinking about scaling that is used in the specific examples in the student edition. This would be a reasonable way to get a general rule without giving up on students' understanding why the general rule makes sense.

Step 1: $\frac{a}{b} = \frac{x}{c}$ a, b, and c represent quantities that are given. The quantity we need to find is x.

Step 2: $\frac{c}{b}$ Compute the scaling factor.

Step 3: $\frac{c}{b} \times a = \frac{c \times a}{b}$ Multiply the scaling factor by a to find the numerator x.

Step 4: $x = \frac{c \times a}{b}$

Using the rule to solve for x in this proportion: $\frac{2}{3} = \frac{x}{4}$, we would compute $x = \frac{2 \times 4}{3} = \frac{8}{3}$, or approximately 2.67. Students may realize this shortcut rule by thinking through a number of specific examples.

For the Teacher When assigning homework, be aware that students may need to do some research on Congress before they answer Exercise 28. Labsheets 4ACE Exercise 27a and 4ACE Exercise 27b are provided for Exercise 27.

Mathematical Goal

- Develop insight and flexibility in choosing strategies for solving problems requiring proportional reasoning

Launch

Use a proportion, such as $\frac{3}{5} = \frac{x}{20}$, to launch the problem.

- *Who can tell us a situation that this proportion might represent?*
- *So, how can we solve this proportion? For $\frac{3}{5} = \frac{x}{20}$, how would you find a scaling factor to make the denominator the same?*
- *So, what do we do with the 4?*
- *So if you apply these ideas to the proportion $\frac{2}{3} = \frac{x}{4}$, how do you solve it?*

Have students work in groups of two or three.

Materials
- Transparency markers

Explore

If students are having difficulty deciding how to find the scaling number in a situation such as Question B, ask:

- *In Question B, we have to solve the proportion $\frac{705}{3} = \frac{x}{240}$. Is the scaling factor for the ratios greater than or less than 1?*
- *So what division will give us the scaling factor?*

Materials
- Graphing calculators

Summarize

Consider commenting and asking:

- *Who can give me a proportion for the jet descending altitude?*
- *Now I need some examples of solution strategies.*

Be sure to look back and compare the solution.

You want students to begin to develop a procedure that will make for efficiency in solving proportions, but do not want to force the issue too far too soon as it will turn off students' thinking and turn on memorization.

Students may need to do some research on Congress before they answer Exercise 28.

Materials
- Student notebooks
- Labsheet 4ACE Exercise 27a

ACE Assignment Guide for Problem 4.3

Differentiated Instruction Solutions for All Learners

Core 6–14

Other *Extensions* 24, 27, 28; unassigned choices from previous problems
Labsheets 4ACE Exercise 27a and 4ACE Exercise 27b are provided if Exercise 27 is assigned.

Adapted For suggestions about adapting ACE exercises, see the CMP *Special Needs Handbook*.

Answers to Problem 4.3

A. 1. $\frac{10}{4,000} = \frac{x}{5,280}$; $\frac{4,000}{10} = \frac{5,280}{x}$; $\frac{10}{x} = \frac{4,000}{5,280}$; $\frac{x}{10} = \frac{5,280}{4,000}$.

2. For $\frac{10}{4,000} = \frac{x}{5,280}$, the scaling factor is $\frac{5,280}{4,000} = 1.32$. So we have $\frac{10 \times 1.32}{4,000 \times 1.32} = \frac{13.2}{5,280}$, and $x = 13.2$ miles.

B. 1. Possible answer: $\frac{705}{3} = \frac{x}{240}$

2. $240 \div 3 = 80$ so the scaling factor is 80. This gives $\frac{705 \times 80}{3 \times 80} = \frac{56,400}{240}$. So Jack eats 56,400 Calories of enchiladas each year.

3. Find the scaling factor by dividing the denominator of the ratio with the unknown by the denominator of the other ratio. Then use the factor to create equivalent ratios that have the same denominator. This allows us to find the solution for x from the numerator of the equivalent ratio.

4. The steps can be used for any ratio with the unknown in the numerator.

5. $705 \div 3 = 235$ Calories for lunch

C. 1. $\frac{58}{172}$; $\frac{76}{172}$; and $\frac{38}{172}$.

2. $\frac{58}{172} = \frac{x}{35}$ so $\frac{58 \times 0.203}{172 \times 0.203} \approx \frac{11.8}{35} \to$ The number of sixth-grade council members should be rounded up to 12.

$\frac{76}{172} = \frac{x}{35}$ so $\frac{76 \times 0.203}{172 \times 0.203} \approx \frac{15.32}{35} \to$ The number of seventh-grade council members should be 15.

$\frac{38}{172} = \frac{x}{35}$ so $\frac{38 \times 0.203}{172 \times 0.203} \approx \frac{7.7}{35} \to$ The number of eighth-grade council members should be rounded up to 8. This gives a total of $8 + 15 + 12 = 35$ representatives.

3. This changes the scaling factor to 0.215. Now we get 0.215×58, 0.215×76, and 0.215×38 as the council members. This gives 12.47 or 12 for sixth grade, 16.34 or 16 for seventh grade, and 8.17 or 8 for eighth grade. The sum of these numbers is $12 + 16 + 8 = 36$. We have to give another representative to one of the grades. Most students will argue to give it to sixth grade since their number was closest to rounding up to 13.

D. 1. $x = 150 \div \frac{8}{284}$

2. $x = 150 \times \frac{284}{8}$, $x = 150(35.50)$, $x = \$5,325$

3. Yes. You can use fact family ideas and division of fractions to write $\frac{a}{b} = \frac{c}{x}$ as $x = c \div \frac{a}{b}$. Since $c \div \frac{a}{b} = c \times \frac{b}{a}$, $x = c \times \frac{b}{a}$.

The student edition pages for this
investigation begin on the next page.

Notes _____

_____

_____

_____

Investigation 4

Making Sense of Proportions

In the following comparison problems, you have information about the relationship between quantities, but one or more specific values are unknown.

- **Calculators** Calculators are on sale at a price of $1,000 for 20. How many can be purchased for $1,250?

- **Similar Figures** The scale factor relating two similar figures is 2. One side of the larger figure is 10 centimeters long. How long is the corresponding side of the smaller figure?

- **Country Music** Country music is the primary format of 20% of American radio stations. There are about 10,600 radio stations in the United States. About how many stations focus on country music?

- **Doctors** Among American doctors, males outnumber females by a ratio of 15 to 4. If about 450,000 doctors are males, about how many are females?

Each of these problems can be solved in several ways. You will learn specific ways to set up ratios for problems like this and find missing values.

48   Comparing and Scaling

Notes _____

_____

_____

_____

There are many ways to solve problems such as the ones on the previous page. One standard way is to create two ratios to represent the information in the problem. Then set these two ratios equal to each other to form a proportion. A **proportion** is an equation that states two ratios are equal.

For example, in the problem about doctors, you have enough information to write one ratio. Then write a proportion to find the missing quantity. There are four different ways to write a proportion representing the data in the problem.

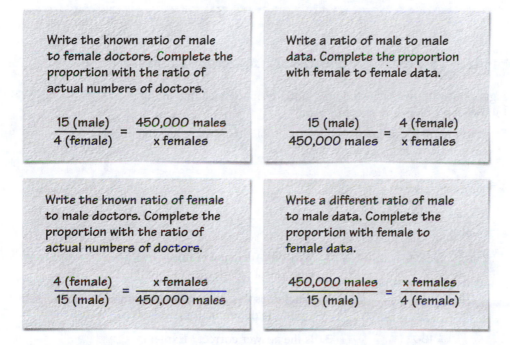

Write the known ratio of male to female doctors. Complete the proportion with the ratio of actual numbers of doctors.

$$\frac{15 \text{ (male)}}{4 \text{ (female)}} = \frac{450,000 \text{ males}}{x \text{ females}}$$

Write a ratio of male to male data. Complete the proportion with female to female data.

$$\frac{15 \text{ (male)}}{450,000 \text{ males}} = \frac{4 \text{ (female)}}{x \text{ females}}$$

Write the known ratio of female to male doctors. Complete the proportion with the ratio of actual numbers of doctors.

$$\frac{4 \text{ (female)}}{15 \text{ (male)}} = \frac{x \text{ females}}{450,000 \text{ males}}$$

Write a different ratio of male to male data. Complete the proportion with female to female data.

$$\frac{450,000 \text{ males}}{15 \text{ (male)}} = \frac{x \text{ females}}{4 \text{ (female)}}$$

Using your knowledge of equivalent ratios, you can now find the number of female doctors from any one of these proportions.

Does any arrangement seem easier than the others?

Notes _____

_____

_____

_____

Analyze the "Similar Figures" problem in the introduction.

The scale factor relating two similar figures is 2. One side of the larger figure is 10 centimeters long. How long is the corresponding side of the smaller figure?

- The scale factor means that the lengths of the sides of the larger figure are 2 times the lengths of the sides of the smaller. What is the ratio of the side lengths of the smaller figure to those of the larger figure?

- Write a proportion to represent the information in the problem.

- Solve your proportion to find the length of the corresponding side of the smaller figure.

Problem 4.1 Setting Up and Solving Proportions

A. Figure out whether each student's thinking about each line in the following problem is correct. Explain.

Dogs outnumber cats in an area by a ratio of 9 to 8. There are 180 dogs in the area. How many cats are there?

Adrianna's Work:

$$\frac{9 \text{ dogs}}{8 \text{ cats}} = \frac{180 \text{ dogs}}{x \text{ cats}}$$

$$\frac{9}{8} \times \frac{20}{20} = \frac{180}{160}$$

$$\frac{180}{160} = \frac{180}{x}$$

$$x = 160$$

1. Why did Adrianna multiply by $\frac{20}{20}$? How did she find what to multiply by?

2. What does this proportion tell you about the denominators? Why?

3. Is the answer correct? Explain.

Joey's Work:

$$\frac{8 \text{ cats}}{9 \text{ dogs}} = \frac{x \text{ cats}}{180 \text{ dogs}}$$

$$\frac{8}{9} = \frac{80}{90} = \frac{160}{180}$$

There are 160 cats.

4. What strategy did Joey use?

5. Why can he make this claim?

Notes _____

_____

_____

_____

B. 1. Calculators are on sale at a price of $1,000 for 20. How many can be purchased for $1,250? Write and solve a proportion that represents the problem. Explain.

2. Country music is the primary format of 20% of American radio stations. There are about 10,600 radio stations in the United States. About how many stations focus on country music?

C. Use the reasoning you applied in Question B to solve these proportions for the variable x. Explain.

1. $\frac{8}{5} = \frac{32}{x}$ **2.** $\frac{7}{12} = \frac{x}{9}$ **3.** $\frac{25}{x} = \frac{5}{7}$ **4.** $\frac{x}{3} = \frac{8}{9}$

D. Use proportions to find the missing lengths in the following similar shapes.

1.

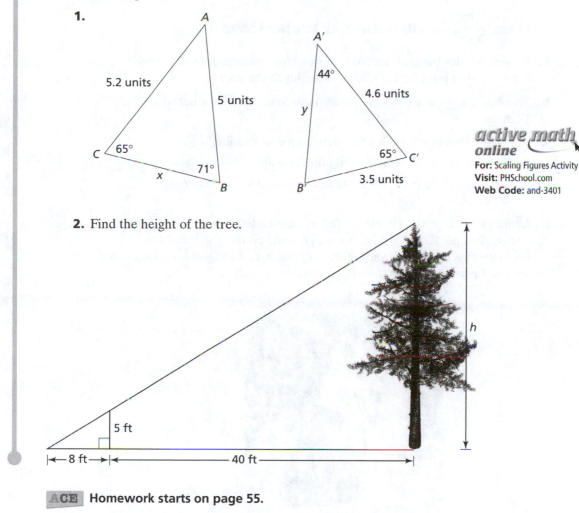

active math
online

For: Scaling Figures Activity
Visit: PHSchool.com
Web Code: and-3401

2. Find the height of the tree.

ACE Homework starts on page 55.

Investigation 4 Making Sense of Proportions   **51**

STUDENT PAGE

STUDENT PAGE

Notes _____

_____

_____

_____

Everyday Use of Proportions

In our everyday lives, we often need to solve proportion problems. So do bakers, tailors, designers, and people in many other occupations.

You may have heard someone say, "A pint is a pound the world around." This saying suggests how to compare liquid measures with weight. It tells us that a pint of liquid weighs about a pound. If you drink a quart of milk a day, you might ask,

> *"About how much does a quart of liquid weigh?"*

Problem 4.2 Applications of Proportions

A. Jogging 5 miles burns about 500 Calories. How many miles will Tanisha need to jog to burn off the 1,200-Calorie lunch she ate?

B. Tanisha jogs about 8 miles in 2 hours. How long will it take her to jog 12 miles?

C. Sam's grandmother says that "a stitch in time saves nine."

    1. What do you think Sam's grandmother means?

    2. Sam's grandmother takes 25 stitches in time. How many does she save?

D. Imani gives vitamins to her dogs. The recommended dosage is 2 teaspoons per day for adult dogs weighing 20 pounds. She needs to give vitamins to Bruiser, who weighs 75 pounds, and to Dust Ball, who weighs 7 pounds. What is the correct dosage for each dog?

STUDENT PAGE

Notes _____

_____

_____

_____

E. The scale factor relating two similar figures is 1.8. One side of the larger figure is 12 centimeters. How long is the corresponding side of the smaller figure?

ACE **Homework starts on page 55.**

4.3 Developing Strategies for Solving Proportions

When mathematicians find the same kind of problem occurring often, they look for a systematic method, or algorithm, that can be applied in each case.

So far in this investigation, you have found ways to solve proportions in specific cases with nice numbers. Now you will develop general strategies that will guide you in solving proportions when the numbers are not so nicely related.

Problem 4.3 Developing Strategies for Solving Proportions

A. A jet takes 10 miles to descend 4,000 feet. How many miles does it take for the jet to descend 5,280 feet?

1. Set up two different proportions that can be solved to answer the question.

2. Solve one of your proportions by whatever method you choose. Check to see that your answer makes sense.

B. Jack works at a restaurant and eats one enchilada for lunch every day that he works. He figures that he ate 240 enchiladas last year. Three enchiladas have a total of 705 Calories. How many Calories did he take in last year from eating enchiladas?

1. Set up a proportion that can be solved to answer the question.

2. Solve your proportion. Check to see that your answer makes sense.

3. Describe each step in your solution strategy.

4. Can your strategy be used to solve any proportion? Explain.

5. How many Calories did he eat for lunch each working day?

Notes _____

_____

_____

_____

C. In Pinecrest Middle School, there are 58 sixth-graders, 76 seventh-graders, and 38 eighth-graders. The school council is made up of 35 students who are chosen to represent all three grades fairly.

    1. Write fractions to represent the part of the school population that is in each grade.

    2. Use these fractions to write and solve proportions that will help you determine a fair number of students to represent each grade on the school council. Explain.

    3. How would the number of students from each grade change if the number of members of the school council were increased to 37? Explain your reasoning.

D. Ms. Spencer needs 150 graphing calculators for her math students. Her budget allows $5,000 for calculators. She needs to know if she can buy what she needs at the discount store where calculators are on sale at 8 for $284.

She writes the following statement:

$$\frac{8}{284} = \frac{150}{x} \quad \text{or} \quad \frac{8}{284} = 150 \div x$$

    1. Use fact-family relationships to rewrite the proportion so that it is easier to find x.

    2. Solve the proportion, recording and explaining each of your steps.

    3. Is your method a general method that can be used to solve any proportion? Explain.

ACE **Homework starts on page 55.**

Notes

Applications

1. Jared and Pedro walk 1 mile in about 15 minutes. They can keep up this pace for several hours.

   a. About how far do they walk in 90 minutes?

   b. About how far do they walk in 65 minutes?

2. Swimming $\frac{1}{4}$ of a mile uses about the same number of Calories as running 1 mile.

   a. Gilda ran a 26-mile marathon. About how far would her sister have to swim to use the same number of Calories Gilda used during the marathon?

   b. Juan swims 5 miles a day. About how many miles would he have to run to use the same number of Calories used during his swim?

3. After testing many samples, an electric company determined that approximately 2 of every 1,000 light bulbs on the market are defective. Americans buy more than 1 billion light bulbs every year. Estimate how many of these bulbs are defective.

4. The organizers of an environmental conference order buttons for the participants. They pay $18 for 12 dozen buttons. Write and solve proportions to answer each question. Assume that price is proportional to the size of the order.

   a. How much do 4 dozen buttons cost?

   b. How much do 50 dozen buttons cost?

   c. How many dozens can the organizers buy for $27?

   d. How many dozens can the organizers buy for $63?

Homework
Help Online
PHSchool.com

For: Help with Exercise 4
Web Code: ane-3404

Investigation 4 Making Sense of Proportions   **55**

Notes _____

_____

_____

_____

5. Denzel makes 10 of his first 15 shots in a basketball free-throw contest. His success rate stays about the same for his next 100 free throws. Write and solve a proportion to answer each part. Round to the nearest whole number. Start each part with the original 10 of 15 free throws.

   a. About how many free throws does Denzel make in his next 60 attempts?

   b. About how many free throws does he make in his next 80 attempts?

   c. About how many attempts does Denzel take to make 30 free throws?

   d. About how many attempts does he take to make 45 free throws?

For Exercises 6–13, solve each equation.

6. $12.5 = 0.8x$

7. $\dfrac{x}{15} = \dfrac{20}{50}$

8. $\dfrac{x}{18} = 4.5$

9. $\dfrac{15.8}{x} = 0.7$

10. $\dfrac{5}{9} = \dfrac{12}{x}$

11. $245 = 0.25x$

12. $\dfrac{18}{x} = \dfrac{4.5}{1}$

13. $\dfrac{0.1}{48} = \dfrac{x}{960}$

Go Online
PHSchool.com
For: Multiple-Choice Skills Practice
Web Code: ana-3454

14. **Multiple Choice** Middletown sponsors a two-day conference for selected middle-school students to study government. There are three middle schools in Middletown.

    Suppose 20 student delegates will attend the conference. Each school should be represented fairly in relation to its population. How many should be selected from each school?

North Middle School
618 students

Central Middle School
378 students

South Middle School
204 students

   A. North: 10 delegates, Central: 8 delegates, South: 2 delegates

   B. North: 11 delegates, Central: 7 delegates, South: 2 delegates

   C. North: 6 delegates, Central: 3 delegates, South: 2 delegates

   D. North: 10 delegates, Central: 6 delegates, South: 4 delegates

Notes _____
_____
_____
_____

Connections

For Exercises 15–17, use ratios, percents, fractions, or rates.

15. **Multiple Choice** Which cereal is the best buy?

    F. a 14-ounce box for $1.98
    G. a 36-ounce box for $2.59
    H. a 1-ounce box for $0.15
    J. a 72-ounce box for $5.25

16. Which is the better average: 10 of 15 free throws, or 8 of 10 free throws?

17. Which is the better home-run rate: two home runs per 60 times at bat, or five home runs per 120 times at bat?

18. A jar contains 150 marked beans. Scott takes several samples from the jar and gets the results shown.

Bean Samples

Number of Beans	25	50	75	100	150	200	250
Number of Marked Beans	3	12	13	17	27	38	52
Percent of Marked Beans	12%	■	■	■	■	■	■

a. Copy and complete the table.

b. Graph the data using (*number of beans, marked beans*) as data points. Describe the pattern of data points in your graph. What does the pattern tell you about the relationship between the number of beans in a sample and the number of marked beans you can expect to find?

19. **Multiple Choice** Ayanna is making a circular spinner to be used at the school carnival. She wants the spinner to be divided so that 30% of the area is blue, 20% is red, 15% is green, and 35% is yellow. Choose the spinner that fits the description.

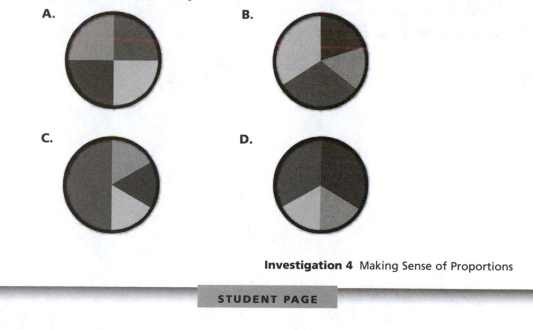

A.

B.

C.

D.

Investigation 4 Making Sense of Proportions   **57**

Notes

20. Hannah is making her own circular spinner. She makes the ratio of green to yellow 2:1, the ratio of red to yellow 3:1, and the ratio of blue to green 2:1. Make a sketch of her spinner.

21. a. Plot the points (8, 6), (8, 22), and (24, 14) on grid paper. Connect them to form a triangle.

   b. Draw the triangle you get when you apply the rule (0.5x, 0.5y) to the three points from part (a).

   c. How are lengths of corresponding sides in the triangles from parts (a) and (b) related?

   d. The area of the smaller triangle is what percent of the area of the larger triangle?

   e. The area of the larger triangle is what percent of the area of the smaller triangle?

22. The sketch shows two similar polygons.

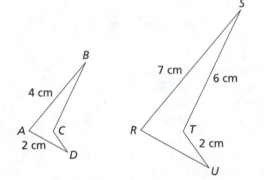

   a. What is the length of side *BC*?

   b. What is the length of side *RU*?

   c. What is the length of side *CD*?

Notes _____

_____

_____

_____

23. To earn an Explorer Scout merit badge, Yoshi and Kai have the task of measuring the width of a river. Their report includes a diagram that shows their work.

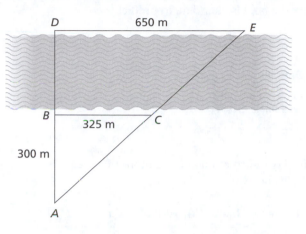

a. How do you think they came up with the lengths of the segments *AB*, *BC*, and *DE*?

b. How can they find the width of the river from segments *AB*, *BC*, and *DE*?

Extensions

24. Angela, a biologist, spends summers on an island in Alaska. For several summers she studied puffins. Two summers ago, Angela captured, tagged, and released 20 puffins. This past summer, she captured 50 puffins and found that 2 of them were tagged. Using Angela's findings, estimate the number of puffins on the island. Explain.

Notes

25. Rita wants to estimate the number of beans in a large jar. She takes out 100 beans and marks them. Then she returns them to the jar and mixes them with the unmarked beans. She then gathers some data by taking a sample of beans from the jar. Use her data to predict the number of beans in the jar.

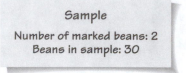

Sample

Number of marked beans: 2
Beans in sample: 30

26. The two histograms below display information about gallons of water used per person in 24 households in a week.

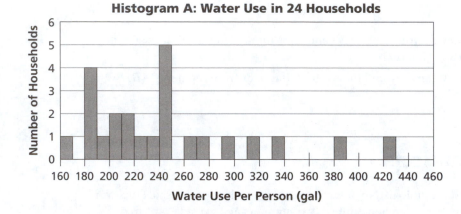

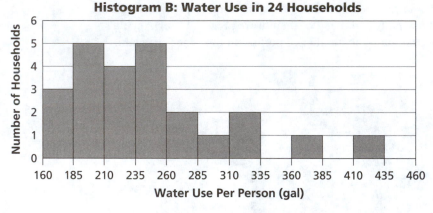

a. Compare the two histograms and explain how they differ.

b. Where do the data seem to clump in Histograms A and B?

Notes _____

_____

_____

_____

27. The picture at the right is drawn on a centimeter grid.

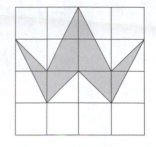

    a. On a grid made of larger squares than those shown here, draw a figure similar to this figure. What is the scale factor between the original figure and your drawing?

    b. Draw another figure similar to this one, but use a grid made of smaller squares than those shown here. What is the scale factor between the original and your drawing?

    c. Compare the perimeters and areas of the original figure and its copies in each case (enlargement and reduction of the figure). Explain how these values relate to the scale factor in each case.

28. The people of the United States are represented in Congress, which is made up of the House of Representatives and the Senate.

    a. In the House of Representatives, the number of representatives from each state varies. From what you know about Congress, how is the number of representatives from each state determined?

    b. How is the number of senators from each state determined?

    c. Compare the two methods of determining representation in Congress. What are the advantages and disadvantages of these two forms of representation for states with large populations? How about for states with small populations?

Investigation 4 Making Sense of Proportions   **61**

Notes _____

_____

_____

_____

Mathematical Reflections 4

In this investigation, you used ratios and proportions to solve a variety of problems. You found that most of those problems can be expressed in proportions such as $\frac{a}{b} = \frac{c}{x}$ or $\frac{a}{b} = \frac{x}{c}$. The next questions will help you summarize what you have learned.

Think about your answers to these questions. Discuss your ideas with other students and your teacher. Then write a summary of your findings in your notebook.

1. For each situation, write a problem that can be solved using a proportion. Then solve your problem.

   a. The fraction of girls in grade seven is $\frac{3}{5}$.

   b. Bolda Cola sells at 5 for $3.

   c. Sora rides her bike at a speed of 12 miles per hour.

   d. A triangle is similar to another one with a scale factor of 1.5.

2. Write four different proportions for the problem you created in part (c). Show that the answer to the problem is the same no matter which proportion you use.

3. What procedures do you use to solve proportions such as those you wrote in Question 2?

Notes _____

_____

_____

_____

Investigation

ACE Assignment Choices

Differentiated Instruction
Solutions for All Learners

Problem 4.1
Core 1, 2, 15–17
Other *Connections* 21–23

Problem 4.2
Core 3–5, 25, 26
Other *Connections* 18–20; unassigned choices from previous problems

Problem 4.3
Core 6–14
Other *Extensions* 24, 27, 28; unassigned choices from previous problems

Adapted For suggestions about adapting Exercise 2 and other ACE exercises, see the CMP *Special Needs Handbook.*
Connecting to Prior Units 18: *Variables and Patterns*; 19–20: *How Likely Is It?, Bits and Pieces III*; 21–23: *Stretching and Shrinking*

Applications

1. **a.** 6 miles. Using equivalent ratios, $\frac{15}{1} = \frac{90}{?}$. The scale factor is 6.

   b. About 4.3 miles. The scale factor is $\frac{13}{3}$, or $4.\overline{3}$.

2. **a.** 6.5 miles. Using equivalent ratios, $\frac{0.25}{1} = \frac{?}{26}$. The scale factor is 26.

   b. 20 miles. Using equivalent ratios, $\frac{0.25}{1} = \frac{5}{?}$. The scale factor is 20.

3. About 2,000,000. Using equivalent fractions, $\frac{2}{1,000} = \frac{?}{1,000,000,000}$.

4. **a.** $6.00. $\frac{\$18}{12 \text{ dozen}} = \frac{?}{4 \text{ dozen}}$. The scale factor is $\frac{1}{3}$. $18 \times \frac{1}{3} = 6$.

b. $75. $\frac{\$18}{12 \text{ dozen}} = \frac{?}{50 \text{ dozen}}$. The scale factor is $\frac{25}{6}$. $18 \times \frac{25}{6} = 75$.

c. 18 dozen. $\frac{\$18}{12 \text{ dozen}} = \frac{27}{?}$. The scale factor is 1.5. $12 \times 1.5 = 18$.

d. 42 dozen. $\frac{\$18}{12 \text{ dozen}} = \frac{\$63}{?}$. The scale factor is 3.5. $3.5 \times 12 = 42$.

5. **a.** 40. Using equivalent fractions, $\frac{10}{15} = \frac{?}{60}$. The scale factor is 4.

   b. About 53.3, or 53. The scale factor is about 5.3.

   c. 45 shots. Using equivalent fractions $\frac{10}{15} = \frac{30}{?}$. The scale factor is 3.

   d. About 68 shots. Using equivalent fractions $\frac{10}{15} = \frac{45}{?}$. The scale factor is 4.5.

6. 15.625. $12.5 \div 0.8 = x; x = 15.625$.

7. 6. $15 \div 50 = 0.3; 0.3 \times 20 = 6$.

8. 81. $4.5 \times 18 = 81$.

9. 22.6. $15.8 \div 0.7 \approx 22.6$.

10. 21.6. $12 \div 5 = 2.4; 2.4 \times 9 = 21.6$.

11. 980. $245 \div 0.25 = 980$.

12. 4. $4.5 \div 18 = 0.25; 1 \div 0.25 = 4$.

13. 2. $960 \div 48 = 20; 0.1 \times 20 = 2$.

14. D. 10.3 (10) from North, 6.3 (6) from Central, and 3.4 (4) from South. The total from all schools is 1,200. The fraction of North to total is $\frac{618}{1,200}$, of Central is $\frac{378}{1,200}$, and of Central is $\frac{204}{1,200}$. Using equivalent fractions, $\frac{618}{1,200} = \frac{?}{20}$. The scale factor is $\frac{1}{60}$. $618 \times \frac{1}{60} = 10.3$, $378 \times \frac{1}{60} = 6.3$, and $204 \times \frac{1}{60} = 3.4$.

(Note: There may be alternative decisions to rounding up 6.3 instead of 3.4. In this instance, the decision was made based on the fact that 3.4 had a greater decimal value than 6.3.)

ACE ANSWERS 4

Connections

15. G

16. $\frac{8}{10} = \frac{4}{5}$ is greater than $\frac{10}{15}$ or $\frac{2}{3}$.

17. 5 out of 120. $\frac{5}{120} = \frac{1}{24} > \frac{2}{60} = \frac{1}{30}$

18. a. (Figure 8)

b.

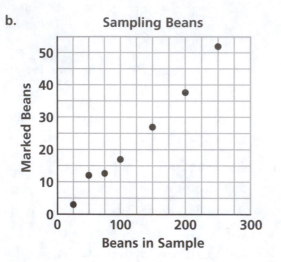

The pattern shows that as the sample size increases, the number of marked beans increases at a fairly steady rate.

19. B

20.

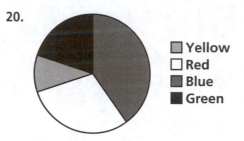

- ☐ Yellow
- ☐ Red
- ☐ Blue
- ■ Green

21. a.

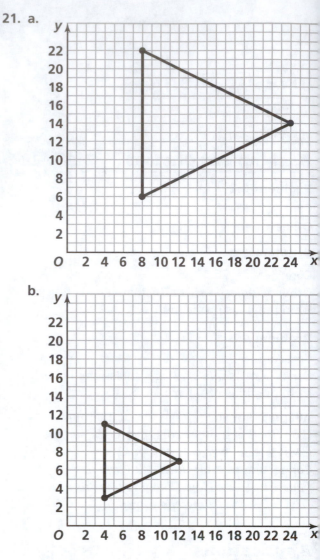

c. The lengths are in proportion. The scale factor between the small triangle and the big triangle is 2 (or the scale factor between the large triangle and the small triangle is 0.5).

d. The area of the small triangle is 25% of the area of the large triangle.

e. The area of the large triangle is 400% of the area of the small triangle.

Figure 8

Bean Samples

Beans in Sample	25	50	75	100	150	200	250
Marked Beans	3	12	13	17	27	38	52
Percent of Marked Beans	12%	24%	≈17.3%	17%	18%	19%	20.8%

22. a. $BC \approx 3.42$. Possible strategies: $\frac{BC}{4} = \frac{6}{7}$.
$BC = \frac{6}{7} \times 4 \approx 3.42$. $\frac{7}{6} = \frac{4}{BC}$. The scale factor is about 0.57. $0.57 \times 6 = 3.42$.

b. $RU = 3.5$. Possible strategies: $\frac{RU}{7} = \frac{2}{4}$.
$RU = 7 \times \frac{2}{4} = 3.5$. $\frac{4}{2} = \frac{7}{RU}$. The scale factor is 1.75. $1.75 \times 2 = 3.5$.

c. $CD \approx 1.14$. Possible strategies: $\frac{CD}{4} = \frac{2}{7}$.
$CD = \frac{2}{7} \times 4 \approx 1.14$. The scale factor is about 0.57. $0.57 \times 2 = 1.14$

23. a. They most likely came up with the segments AB, BC, and DE by measuring. They could have used measuring tools or instruments to determine the length of segments they made. They probably staked off two points and measured the distance between them.

b. Using equivalent ratios, based on the fact that the triangles are similar (Triangle ADE is similar to Triangle ABC). For example, 650:325 as $DB + BA$: 300 or $\frac{650}{325} = \frac{DB + BA}{300}$. The scale factor is about 0.923. $0.923 \times 650 \approx 600$. $600 - BA$ (which is known to be 300) = 300. Therefore, they could reason that the river was about 300 feet.

Extensions

24. 500. Using equivalent fractions, $\frac{2}{50} = \frac{20}{?}$. The scale factor is 10.

25. About 1,500 beans. Using equivalent fractions $\frac{x}{100} = \frac{30}{2}$. The scale factor is 50.

26. a. Histogram B uses larger intervals, so more households fit in each interval and the bars go higher. Histogram B is slightly more uniform on the lower end, while Histogram A overall contains more gaps and is not as uniform.

b. Possible answers: In Histogram A, the data seem to clump from 180 to 250 gallons, and in Histogram B, the data seem to clump from 160 to 260.

27. a–b. One possible example is a picture that is either enlarged by a scale factor of 4 (going from the smaller figure to the

larger figure), or reduced by a scale factor of $\frac{1}{4}$ (going from the larger figure to the smaller figure).

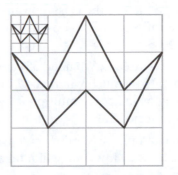

Note: Other scale factors could be used.

c. The perimeter of the similar figures can be found by multiplying the original scale factor by the corresponding scale factor of either the enlargement or the reduction. In the above example, the scale factor for the perimeter of the enlargement is 4 and the scale factor for the perimeter of the reduction is $\frac{1}{4}$. The area of the two similar figures is found by multiplying the area of one figure by the square of the scale factor to determine the area of the other similar figure. In the example above, the scale factor for the area of the enlargement is 4^2 and the area for the reduced figure is $(\frac{1}{4})^2$ or $\frac{1}{16}$.

28. a. The number of representatives from each state is determined by the ratio of the population of the state to the population in the United States. Therefore, the greater the population of a state, the more representatives that state will have. Note: there is a minimum number of representatives so small states are still better represented proportionately than large states.

b. The number of senators is the same for every state, regardless of size or population. It is 2 per state.

c. With the same number for every state, small states can get an equal say/voice/vote, in terms of the Senate. However, with the method of the House of Representatives, the large states get more representation or voice, thus the Congress would be reflecting the voice of the people.

Possible Answers to Mathematical Reflections

1. **a.** Various answers. One possibility is: There are 15 girls in the class, how many boys? The ratio of girls to boys is 3 to 2. This gives $15 \div 3 = 5, 5 \times 2 = 10$ boys.

   b. An example is: We need 35 cans of Bolda Cola. How much will it cost? There are seven 5s in 35. We multiply 7 by $3 to get the price of $21.

   c. An example is: Sora's friend lives 4 mi from her house. How long will it take Sora to ride her bike to her friend's house? $\frac{12}{4} = \frac{60}{20}$. Therefore it will take 20 min.

   d. An example is: The small triangle has a side of length 3 cm. How long is the corresponding side in the larger triangle? $1.5 \times 3 = 4.5$ cm.

2. $\frac{12}{60} = \frac{4}{x}; \frac{12}{4} = \frac{60}{x}; \frac{60}{12} = \frac{x}{4}; \frac{4}{12} = \frac{x}{60}$

3. Procedures that can be used to solve proportions include finding equivalent ratios or equivalent fractions. Another method would be to find a scale factor or a unit rate.

Answers to Looking Back and Looking Ahead

1. **a.** *Difference*: this is done by subtracting the number of walkers from the number of bus riders, which answers the question of "How many more ride the bus than walk?" For Mr. Archer's room the difference is 5.

   Ratio: can also be used to compare the number of bus riders to the number of walkers. For Mr. Archer's room, the ratio is 20 : 15 or 4 : 3.

   Fractions: done by writing the number of walkers out of the total students from the room and then the number of bus riders out of the total students from the room and comparing. For Mr. Archer's room, the fractions are $\frac{4}{7}$ bus riders and $\frac{3}{7}$ walkers.

   Percent: can also be used to determine the number of bus riders and walkers out of 100. For Mr. Archer's room, the percent of bus riders is 57% and the percent of walkers is 43%.

   Unit rate or *scaling*: can be used by dividing the number of walkers into the number of bus riders and determining that there are about 1.3 bus riders for every walker, or the number of bus riders is about 1.3 times the number of walkers.

   The best statement would probably be the *ratio*, as you are trying to compare two parts, bus riders to walkers.

   b. One could compare the number of bus riders and walkers between homerooms through use of percents. Percents allow comparison of both bus riders and walkers to be out of 100, so that the differences in total students between the homerooms would not matter. Mr. Archer's homeroom had 57% bus riders and 43% walkers as compared to 61% bus riders and 39% walkers from Ms. Brown's. The ratio of bus riders to walkers can be compared between rooms, such as 4 to 3 for Mr. Archer's and 14 to 9 for Ms. Brown's (or 12 to 9 for Mr. Archer's and 14 to 9 for Ms. Brown's). A comparison can also be made by the unit rate or scale factor, so determine the number of walkers per bus rider or bus riders per walkers for each homeroom; 1.3 bus riders per walker for Mr. Archer and 1.6 bus riders per walker for Ms. Brown. The difference between bus riders and walkers could also be compared between homerooms. The difference is 5 for Mr. Archer's and 5 for Ms. Brown's. The best method seems to be the percent, as the number of students in each homeroom is not the same and therefore to be able to make a comparison on unlike quantities, percents work the best because it places the numbers in amounts "out of 100."

   c. 12. Using equivalent ratios, $\frac{5}{3} = \frac{20}{?}$. The scale factor is 4.

   d. 180 bus riders and 120 walkers. The total bus riders from the 3 homerooms is 54 and the total walkers from the 3 homerooms is 36. The total number of students in the 3 homerooms is 90. Using equivalent fractions, for bus riders, $\frac{54}{90} = \frac{?}{300}$. The scale factor is $3\frac{1}{3}$.

   e. 270 bus riders and 180 walkers. The ratio of bus riders to walkers at East is 3 to 2.

2. **a.** Dog food. Dog food costs 49 cents per pound and cat food costs 60 cents per pound.

b. A cat is cheapest to feed. The cost per pound of cat food is 60 cents and a cat eats $\frac{1}{3}$ pound a day; therefore, it costs 20 cents a day to feed a cat. Dog food costs 49 cents per pound. A small dog eats $\frac{1}{2}$ pound a day and therefore costs about 25 cents a day, while a large dog eats $1\frac{1}{4}$ pounds a day and therefore costs about 61 cents a day to feed.

c. Cat food. For cat food, $20 \times (\frac{1}{3}) = 6\frac{2}{3}$ lb per day. Since the bag holds 10 lb, it will last $10 \div 6\frac{2}{3} = 1.5$ days. For dog food, $30 \times (\frac{1}{2}) + 20 \times (1\frac{1}{4}) = 40$ lb/day used. Since the bag holds 50 lb, it will last $50 \div 40 = 1.25$ days.

d. About 20.67 bags of cat food (21 opened) and 24.8 bags of dog food (25 opened). There are 31 days in January. Since 1 bag of dog food lasts 1.25 days, 24.8 bags will be needed. Since 1 bag of cat food lasts 1.5 days, 20.67 bags will be needed.

e. The 50-lb bag will cost $22.50. At the new store, the cost of Bow Chow per pound is 45 cents ($0.45). Therefore, for 50 lb, it will cost $0.45 \times 50 = \$22.50$.

f. The new store is a better deal. It costs $22.50 for a 50-lb bag, but at the old store it costs $24.50. Therefore, the owner will save $2 on a 50-lb bag if he/she shops at the new store.

3. You need to look at what the question is asking. Ratios are used when you are comparing two quantities, such as two parts of a mix and want to know the scale between them. Percentages are used when you compare two things in different amounts. Differences are used when you talk about a discrepancy between two amounts. Rates are used when you want to talk about a direct comparison between two sets. When you want to compare number of girls to number of boys, a ratio would be appropriate. When you want to know how much bigger or farther one thing is from another, using differences is appropriate. When you want to know the number of something per some other unit, such as the number of calories per cookie, then a rate would be appropriate. When you want to know how many people out of 100, then a percentage would be appropriate.

4. 3 to 5 can also be expressed as 3 : 5. One can express it using the fraction $\frac{3}{5}$, or the percent 60%. 3 to 5 can also be expressed as 0.6 per unit.

5. a. 12 to 9, 4 to 3, 240 to 180, 8 to 6, 48 to 36

b. 4 to 3

6. Find the scale factor between the two given numbers in the same numerator or denominator location and then multiply by the scale factor. For example, to solve $\frac{5}{8} = \frac{12}{?}$, find the scale factor between 12 and 5 ($12 \div 5 = 2.4$), then multiply 8 by 2.4, which is 19.2. To solve, $\frac{5}{8} = \frac{?}{24}$, find the scale factor between 24 and 8 ($24 \div 8 = 3$) and multiply 5 by the scale factor (15). Strategies include finding the scale factor or equivalent fractions.

7. a. With the recipe, you scale up or down the quantity of ingredients needed based on the number of people you need to serve and the number of people the recipe can feed in original form. To change recipes to meet the number of people, you would need to multiply the amount of each ingredient by the ratio of the number of people you want to feed to the number of people you can feed per the original recipe. For example, to scale up a recipe that serves 4 to serve 12, multiply 3 by each quantity of ingredient listed. Similarly, to scale down a recipe that serves 20 to serve 4, multiply each quantity of ingredient by $\frac{4}{20}$ (or $\frac{1}{5}$).

b. Compare the difference on the map and use the scale factor given in the legend to determine the actual distance (multiply the difference you find on a map using a ruler by the ratio/scale factor given on the map). For example, the distance between two cities on a map is 0.25 inches. If the scale factor is 1 inch = 100 miles, then the actual distance is 25 miles.

c. Use proportion to determine the cost per unit of weight (ounces or pounds). Then the unit rates of cost per weight can be compared to determine which is the better deal or more economical.

d. You can multiply the coordinates by scale factors to make larger or smaller copies of the design. The copies would then be similar to the original. The scale factor would be the ratio of one side of the design to the corresponding side of a similar figure of the design.

Investigation 4 Making Sense of Proportions **93**

Assigning the Unit Project

The optional Unit Project provides an opportunity for students to further develop their understanding of ratio and proportion. This section contains preparation notes for the Paper Pool project, answers, and a holistic-by-category scoring rubric with guidelines for how it can be used to assess the project. Samples of two students' work and a teacher's comments accompany the suggested rubric.

Preparing for the Unit Project

For this project, students are asked to play a game called Paper Pool. The game is played on rectangular square-grid tables, such as the one shown here.

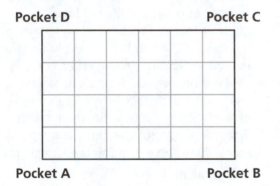

Pocket D   **Pocket C**

Pocket A   **Pocket B**

An imaginary ball is hit from the lower left-hand corner, Pocket A, at a 45° angle. A ball hit in this way will bounce each side it hits at a 45° angle. The ball continues to roll until it hits a pocket. Pockets are located at each corner of the table. Students play paper pool on different-sized rectangular tables.

Students are to predict the pocket in which the ball will stop and how many hits (anything making contact with the ball—the sides of the table, the imaginary cue, the pocket) will occur by the time the ball comes to a stop (reaches a pocket).

To do the task, students will need to investigate several sizes of Paper Pool tables. They will need to gather and organize data and search for patterns. Finding a solution will require students to recognize relationships between rectangles whose sides have the same ratio.

We recommend that the project be started near the end of the unit (after Investigation 3 or 4).

Materials

- Unit Project Student's Guide Parts (A)–(D)
- Paper Pool Labsheets A–C
- centimeter grid paper
- colored pencils or markers

Goals for Students

- gather and organize data
- search for patterns
- recognize rectangles whose sides have the same ratio (similar rectangles)
- use the simplest ratio to predict the stopping pocket and number of hits.

Launch

Distribute the Unit Project labsheets, and review the task introduction with your students. Make sure they understand how the ball travels on the Paper Pool tables and how to count the number of hits that occur on any table. Check that the students have drawn the paths correctly for the two sample tables.

An extension question is offered with this task. You may want to assign it to everyone, or you may use it as an extra challenge for those groups that want to investigate patterns further.

Explore

We recommend that students work on this project with a partner. One class period will be needed for students to collect their data. They can continue to investigate the task and draft their reports outside of class. Part of a second class period may be used for comparing results and finalizing reports.

Summarize

You may want to have students share their results. If the extension question was given as an extra challenge, be sure to ask any students who attempted it to share their results.

Grading the Unit Project

The Paper Pool project is an open-ended investigation with a wide range of possible observations that students could make. In the project, students are asked to find patterns and write rules about how the ball travels on Paper Pool tables.

Possible Student Responses

Some students may give rules that are related to a specific example, while others may give rules that generalize across several different rectangles. In the examples that follow, we call a rule that works for all tables with a specific characteristic in common (such as a horizontal length of 1 and a vertical length that is an even number) a "specific" rule. Rules that look beyond a single common characteristic and apply to a more general category, we call "sophisticated" rules.

Possible Rules for Predicting the Dropping Pocket

Specific rules Specific rules usually involve only one variable.

- If the table is a square, the ball will stop at Pocket C.
- If the table has a horizontal dimension of 1 unit and a vertical dimension that is an odd number, the ball will stop at Pocket C.
- If the table has a horizontal dimension of 1 unit and a vertical dimension that is an even number, the ball will stop at Pocket D.
- If the table has a vertical dimension of 1 unit and a horizontal dimension that is an odd number, the ball will stop at Pocket C.
- If the table has a vertical dimension of 1 unit and a horizontal dimension that is an even number, the ball will stop at Pocket B.
- The ball will never stop at Pocket A.
- In all similar rectangles of the same orientation, the ball will stop at the same pocket.

Sophisticated rules Sophisticated rules compare more than one variable.

In all similar rectangles of the same orientation, the ball will stop at the same pocket. The pocket is determined by the ratio of the table's sides. If the ratio of the horizontal dimension to the vertical dimension is:

- an odd number to an odd number, the ball will drop in Pocket C.
- an odd number to an even number, the ball will drop in Pocket D.
- an even number to an odd number, the ball will drop in Pocket B.

Possible Rules for Predicting the Number of Hits

Specific rules Specific rules usually involve only one variable.

- If the table is a square, there will be two hits.
- If the table has a side length of 1, the number of hits will be 1 greater than the length of the other side (or, the number of hits will be the sum of the two sides).
- For all similar rectangles, the number of hits is the same.

Sophisticated rules Sophisticated rules compare more than one variable.

For all similar rectangles, the number of hits is the same. The number of hits is the sum of the numbers of the simplified ratio (to the least whole-number amounts) of the table's sides.

Suggested Scoring Rubric

This rubric employs a point scale for four different areas of assessment for a total of 21 possible points. The rubric does *not assess* students' work on the optional extension question.

MATHEMATICS: RULES FOR PREDICTING THE DROPPING POCKET (4 points possible)

4 Student states at least one correct sophisticated rule and addresses all possible situations for which pocket the ball will drop.

3 Student states one correct sophisticated rule and/or several specific rules that address several possible situations for where the ball will drop.

2 Student states at least two correct specific rules.

1 Student shows evidence of searching for a pattern but states no original pattern or rule OR student states one specific rule.

0 Student did not engage; no patterns or rules are given.

MATHEMATICS: RULES FOR PREDICTING THE TOTAL NUMBER OF HITS (4 points possible)

4 Student states at least one correct sophisticated rule and addresses all possible situations for the number of hits.

3 Student states one correct sophisticated rule and/or several specific rules that address several possible situations for the number of hits.

2 Student states at least two correct specific rules.

1 Student shows evidence of searching for a pattern but states no original pattern or rule OR student states one correct specific rule.

0 Student did not engage; no patterns or rules are given.

PROBLEM SOLVING AND REASONING (4 points possible)

4 Student shows complete reasoning to support at least one sophisticated rule for both situations.

3 Student shows adequate reasoning to support given sophisticated rule(s) or gives complete reasoning to support specific rules for both situations.

2 Student shows reasoning about rules through words or organizational instruments but the reasoning is weak (tests an inadequate variety of situations and draws conclusions that would require testing more cases or examining more varied arrangements) OR student has only one or two specific rules and does not address both situations.

1 Student shows reasoning about rules through words or organizational instruments but the reasoning may be faulty (incorrect logic or nonsensical statements in the context of the problem) OR student reasons through only one specific rule.

0 Student does not engage in the task.

COMMUNICATION (4 points possible)

4 Report is clearly presented and easy to follow.

3 With some extra effort, the reader can follow the student's report.

2 Significant effort is needed to follow the student's report.

1 Student does not address the task.

0 Student does not communicate in any form.

CHECKLIST (5 points possible)

- Student completes Labsheets Paper Pool A–C (1 point).

- Student gives a correct new table for each rule and gives at least two rules (2 points) OR student gives one rule and one correct new table that fits the rule (1 point).

- Student uses organizational tool(s) to search for patterns and rules. (Quality is the determining factor for giving a paper 1 or 2 points.)

A Teacher's Comments

I had my students work in pairs, but each had to write his or her own report. I used the suggested time schedule; one class period and then half of a class period three days later. This allowed students who needed more time to investigate the situation and look for patterns to do so at home. The half period of class was used to discuss and revise reports as partners shared what each had written. Most of my students found this project interesting and were very engaged in the mathematical investigation.

The students' reports came in several forms and levels of quality. The two projects below are examples of student work from the class. (The students' labsheets and any additional drawings they did are not included.) The work was scored using the suggested rubric provided. An explanation of the scores for each of the two projects is written after each example.

Sample #1

Mary Beth

We discovered that before you can really find rules you have to convert the paper pool tables into basic tables, or smallest form. As we did that we realized that there would be no even by even dimensions because they can be broken down. The possible dimensions are odd by odd, odd by even, and even by odd. Odd by even and even by odd dimensions are different because the pockets would be in different corners. The odd by odd dimensions always end in the C pocket, odd by even in B, and even by odd in D. To find how many hits there will be, add the dimensions. The total will also include the starting and finishing pockets.

A Teacher's Comments on Sample 1

Mary Beth's project received eight of the eight possible points for the mathematics in her report. Her rule for the dropping pocket covers all possible cases. She notes that it makes a difference whether the table is odd by even or even by odd, but she does not tell whether she is giving the horizontal dimension or the vertical dimension first. Her drawings and organizational tools (she made tables to organize her information) made it possible to determine what she meant, so full credit for her rules was given.

A four was given for her sophisticated rule for the number of hits that would occur. Her rule identifies the sum of the dimensions of the table as the important relationship that allows you to find out the total number of hits that will occur. However, her written report does not state that it is the sum of the dimensions when expressed as a ratio in simplest form (or what she calls earlier, "basic" form). I might have counted down for the omission were it not for the fact that her labsheets, new drawings, and organizational tools showed that she understood this.

Mary Beth received four points for problem solving and reasoning. Her reasoning for her rules was complete when I took into account her written summary, new drawings, and organizational tools. She received only three points for communication because of the effort needed by the reader to sort out which side she was referring to in her odd-by-even and even-by-odd rules. The score also reflects the lack of clarity and completeness in her description of her dropping-pocket rule.

Mary Beth's new table, labsheet, and organizational tool were included in her report, and she was given all the points for this section due to their quality and completeness. Mary Beth received 20 of the 21 points and was given an A for the project.

MATHEMATICS	dropping-pocket rule	4 out of 4
	total hits rule	4 out of 4
PROBLEM SOLVING & REASONING		4 out of 4
COMMUNICATION		3 out of 4
CHECKLIST	new tables	2 out of 2
	completed labsheets	1 out of 1
	organizational tools	2 out of 2
TOTAL POINTS		20 out of 21

Sample #2

Heather

* For a 1 by any odd number it will end up at C.
* For a 1 by any even number it will end up at B.
* If one side is twice as big as the other side it will hit once & end up at B.
* When it is a square it will not hit a side, but go to diagonal corner C.
* On an odd by odd it will always end up at corner C & hit as many times as possibal.
* If 1 demention is 4 x larger or ¼ the other, it hits 3 times & lands in B.
* Nothing ends up in A.

A Teacher's Comments on Sample 2

Heather's project received five of the eight points for the mathematics in her report. A three was given for six basic rules and one sophisticated rule that identified the dropping pocket. A two was given for her three basic rules for the number of hits. (A fourth rule, "two hits," is started but not finished.) Her rules for the dropping pocket cover several possibilities, and her rule, "On an odd by odd it will always end up at corner C," is considered a sophisticated rule. She does not address the orientation of the rectangle, and the reader can make sense of her rules only by examining her drawings and organizational tools. Heather's rules for the dropping pocket suggest that she looked for patterns. Her rules for the number of hits are part of some of her rules for dropping pockets. The count she gives for the number of hits is incorrect and suggests that she does not understand what counts as a hit. It seems that she has not counted the hit from the imaginary cue, nor the hit at the last pocket.

Because Heather shows no evidence of being able to reason about how many hits will occur, and because the reader's only evidence of Heather's reasoning is through her labsheets and single organization chart, she was given a two for problem solving and reasoning. A two was given for communication because the reader must make a significant effort to follow her report. Because Heather does not deal with the orientation of the rectangles, one must make an effort to sort through her work and make sense of the rules she has given.

Heather's new tables to demonstrate her rules were complete and she received two points for them. Her labsheets were also complete, so she received the one point for including these papers in her report. She received one point for her organizational tools, which included only a table that organized the information about the dropping pocket. She did not include an organizational tool addressing the number of hits.

Heather's work was given 13 of 21 points and a grade of a C. Her labsheets show that she is not counting the number of hits correctly. I'm not sure why this is because when we launched the project in class, both she and her partner correctly counted the number of hits for the sample Paper Pool tables in the launch. Further instruction will probably be needed to help the partners address the issue of hits. I will also want to talk to Heather and all the students about how to look for patterns and how to organize information to help in looking for patterns.

MATHEMATICS dropping-pocket rule		3 out of 4
	total hits rule	2 out of 4
PROBLEM SOLVING & REASONING		2 out of 4
COMMUNICATION		2 out of 4
CHECKLIST	new tables	2 out of 2
	completed labsheets	1 out of 1
	organizational tools	1 out of 2
TOTAL POINTS		13 out of 21

Unit Project

Paper Pool

The unit project is a mathematical investigation of a game called Paper Pool. For a pool table, use grid paper rectangles like the one shown at the right. Each outside corner is a pocket where a "ball" could "fall."

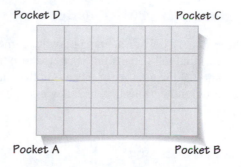

Pocket D   Pocket C

Pocket A   Pocket B

How to Play Paper Pool

- The ball always starts at Pocket A.
- To move the ball, "hit" it as if you were playing pool.
- The ball always moves on a 45° diagonal across the grid.
- When the ball hits a side of the table, it bounces off at a 45° angle and continues to move.
- If the ball moves to a corner, it falls into the pocket at that corner.

The dotted lines on the table at the right show the ball's path.

- The ball falls in Pocket D.
- There are five "hits," including the starting hit and the final hit.
- The dimensions of the table are 6 by 4 (always mention the horizontal length first).

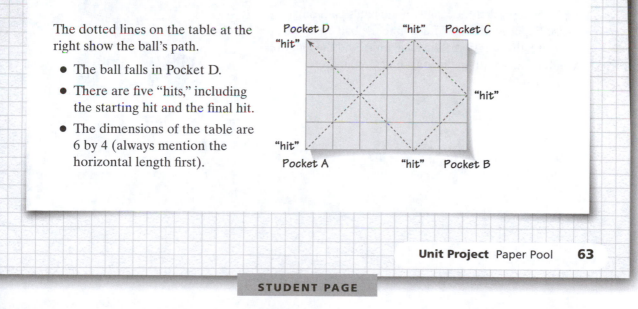

Unit Project Paper Pool   **63**

Notes _____

Part 1: Investigate Two Questions

Use the three Paper Pool labsheets to play the game. Try to find rules that tell you (1) the pocket where the ball will fall and (2) the number of hits along the way. Keep track of the dimensions because they may give you clues to a pattern.

Part 2: Write a Report

When you find some patterns and reach some conclusions, write a report that includes

- A list of the rules you found and an explanation of why you think they are correct
- Drawings of other grid paper tables that follow your rule
- Any tables, charts, or other tools that helped you find patterns
- Other patterns or ideas about Paper Pool

Extension Question

Can you predict the length of the ball's path on any size Paper Pool table? Each time the ball crosses a square, the length is 1 diagonal unit. Find the length of the ball's path in diagonal units for any set of dimensions.

active math
online

For: Paper Pool Activity
Visit: PHSchool.com
Web Code: and-3000

Notes _____

_____

_____

_____

Looking Back and Looking Ahead

The problems in this unit required you to compare measured quantities. You learned when it seems best to use subtraction, division, percents, rates, ratios, and proportions to make those comparisons. You developed a variety of strategies for writing and solving proportions. These strategies include writing equivalent ratios to scale a ratio up or down. You also learned to compute and reason with unit rates.

Go Online
PHSchool.com

For: Vocabulary Review Puzzle
Web Code: anj-3051

Use Your Understanding: Proportional Reasoning

Test your understanding of percents, rates, ratios, and proportions by solving the following problems.

1. There are 300 students in East Middle School. To plan transportation services for the new West Middle School, the school system surveyed East students. The survey asked whether students ride a bus to school or walk.

   - In Mr. Archer's homeroom, 20 students ride the bus and 15 students walk.
   - In Ms. Brown's homeroom, 14 students ride the bus and 9 students walk.
   - In Mr. Chavez's homeroom, 20 students ride the bus and the ratio of bus riders to walkers is 5 to 3.

   a. In what ways can you compare the number of students in Mr. Archer's homeroom who are bus riders to the number who are walkers? Which seems to be the best comparison statement?

   b. In what ways can you compare the numbers of bus riders and walkers in Ms. Brown's homeroom to those in Mr. Archer's homeroom? Again, which seems the best way to make the comparison?

   c. How many students in Mr. Chavez's homeroom walk to school?

Notes _____

_____

_____

_____

STUDENT PAGE

d. Use the information from these three homerooms. About how many East Middle School students would you expect to walk to school? How many would you expect to ride a bus?

e. Suppose the new West Middle School will have 450 students and a ratio of bus riders to walkers that is about the same as that in East Middle School. About how many West students can be expected in each category?

2. The Purr & Woof Kennel buys food for animals that are boarded. The amounts of food eaten and the cost for food are shown below.

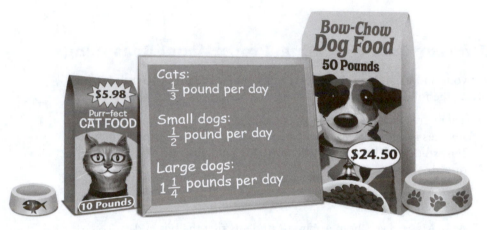

a. Is cat food or dog food cheaper per pound?

b. Is it cheapest to feed a cat, a small dog, or a large dog?

c. On an average day, the kennel has 20 cats, 30 small dogs, and 20 large dogs. Which will last longer: a bag of cat food or a bag of dog food?

d. How many bags of dog food will be used in the month of January? How many bags of cat food will be used?

e. The owner finds a new store that sells Bow-Chow in 15 pound bags for $6.75 per bag. How much does that store charge for 50 pounds of Bow-Chow?

f. Which is a better buy on Bow-Chow: the original source or the new store?

66 Comparing and Scaling

STUDENT PAGE

Notes _____

_____

_____

_____

Explain Your Reasoning

Answering comparison questions often requires knowledge of rates, ratios, percents, and proportional reasoning. Answer the following questions about your reasoning strategies. Use the preceding problems and other examples from this unit to illustrate your ideas.

3. How do you decide when to compare numbers using ratios, rates, or percents rather than by finding the difference of the two numbers?

4. Suppose you are given information that the ratio of two quantities is 3 to 5. How can you express that relationship in other written forms?

5. Suppose that the ratio of two quantities is 24 to 18.

    a. State five other equivalent ratios in the form "p to q."

    b. Use whole numbers to write an equivalent ratio that cannot be scaled down without using fractions or decimals.

6. What strategies can you use to solve proportions such as $\frac{5}{8} = \frac{12}{x}$ and $\frac{5}{8} = \frac{x}{24}$?

7. How does proportional reasoning enter into the solution of each problem?

    a. You want to prepare enough of a recipe to serve a large crowd.

    b. You want to use the scale of a map to find the actual distance between two points in a park from their locations on the map.

    c. You want to find which package of raisins is the better value.

    d. You want to use a design drawn on a coordinate grid to make several larger copies and several smaller copies of that design.

Look Ahead

Proportional reasoning is an important way to compare measured quantities. It includes comparing numerical information by ratios, rates, and percents. It is used in geometry to enlarge and reduce figures while retaining their shapes. You will apply proportional reasoning in future *Connected Mathematics* units such as *Filling and Wrapping*, *Moving Straight Ahead*, and *What Do You Expect?*

Notes _____

_____

_____

_____

P

proportion An equation stating that two ratios are equal. For example:

$$\frac{\text{hours spent on homework}}{\text{hours spent in school}} = \frac{2}{7}$$

Note that this does not necessarily imply that hours spent on homework = 2 or that hours spent in school = 7. During a week, 10 hours may have been spent on homework while 35 hours were spent in school. The proportion is still true because $\frac{10}{35} = \frac{2}{7}$.

proporción Una ecuación que indica que dos razones son iguales. Por ejemplo:

$$\frac{\text{horas dedicadas a la tarea}}{\text{horas en la escuela}} = \frac{2}{7}$$

Fíjate que esto no implica necesariamente que las horas dedicadas a la tarea = 2, ó que las horas en la escuela = 7. Durante una semana, puedes haber pasado 10 horas haciendo tarea y 35 horas en la escuela. La proporción sigue siendo verdadera porque $\frac{10}{35} = \frac{2}{7}$.

R

rate A comparison of quantities measured in two different units is called a rate. A rate can be thought of as a direct comparison of two sets (20 cookies for 5 children) or as an average amount (4 cookies per child). A rate such as 5.5 miles per hour can be written as $\frac{5.5 \text{ miles}}{1 \text{ hour}}$, or 5.5 miles : 1 hour.

tasa Una comparación de cantidades medidas en dos unidades diferentes se llama tasa. Una tasa se puede interpretar como una comparación directa entre dos grupos (20 galletas para 5 niños) o como una cantidad promedio (4 galletas por niño). Una tasa como 5.5 millas por hora se puede escribir como $\frac{5.5 \text{ millas}}{1 \text{ hora}}$, o como 5.5 millas a 1 hora.

rate table You can use a rate to find and organize equivalent rates in a rate table. For example, you can use the rate "five limes for $1.00" to make this rate table.

tabla de tasas Puedes usar una tasa para hallar y organizar tasas equivalentes en una tabla de tasas. Por ejemplo, puedes usar la tasa "cinco limas por $1.00" para hacer esta tabla de tasas, en la cual se indica el número de limas y el costo de las limas.

Cost of Limes

Number of Limes	1	2	3	4	5	10	15	20
Cost of Limes	$0.20	$0.40	$0.60	$0.80	$1.00	$2.00	$3.00	$4.00

Notes _____

_____

_____

_____

ratio A ratio is a number, often expressed as a fraction, used to make comparisons between two quantities. Ratios may also be expressed as equivalent decimals or percents, or given in the form $a : b$. Here are some examples of uses of ratios:

- The ratio of females to males on the swim team is 2 to 3, or $\frac{2 \text{ females}}{3 \text{ males}}$.
- The train travels at a speed of 80 miles per hour, or $\frac{80 \text{ miles}}{1 \text{ hour}}$.
- If a small figure is enlarged by a scale factor of 2, the new figure will have an area four times its original size. The ratio of the small figure's area to the large figure's area will be $\frac{1}{4}$. The ratio of the large figure's area to the small figure's area will be $\frac{4}{1}$, or 4.
- In the example above, the ratio of the length of a side of the small figure to the length of the corresponding side of the large figure is $\frac{1}{2}$. The ratio of the length of a side of the large figure to the length of the corresponding side of the small figure is $\frac{2}{1}$, or 2.

razón Una razón es un número, a menudo expresado como fracción, que se usa para hacer comparaciones entre dos cantidades. Las razones también se pueden expresar como decimales equivalentes o porcentajes, o darse de la forma $a : b$. Estos son algunos ejemplos del uso de razones:

- La razón entre mujeres y hombres en el equipo de natación es 2 a 3, es decir, $\frac{2 \text{ mujeres}}{3 \text{ hombres}}$.
- El tren viaja a una velocidad de 80 millas por hora, o sea, $\frac{80 \text{ millas}}{1 \text{ hora}}$.
- Si se amplía una figura pequeña por un factor de escala 2, la nueva figura tendrá un área cuatro veces mayor que su tamaño original. La razón entre el área de la figura pequeña y el área de la figura grande será $\frac{1}{4}$. La razón entre el área de la figura grande y el área de la figura pequeña será $\frac{4}{1}$, o sea, 4.
- En el ejemplo anterior, la razón entre la longitud de un lado de la figura pequeña y la longitud del lado correspondiente de la figura grande es $\frac{1}{2}$. La razón entre la longitud de un lado de la figura grande y la longitud del lado correspondiente de la figura pequeña es $\frac{2}{1}$, o sea, 2.

S

scale, scaling The scale is the number used to multiply both parts of a ratio to produce an equal, but possibly more informative, ratio. A ratio can be scaled to produce a number of equivalent ratios. For example, multiplying the rate of 4.5 gallons per hour by a scale of 2 yields the rate of 9 gallons per 2 hours. Scales are also used on maps to give the relationship between a measurement on the map to the actual physical measurement.

escala, aplicar una escala La escala es el número que se usa para multiplicar las dos partes de una razón para producir una razón igual, pero posiblemente más informativa. Se puede aplicar una escala a una razón para producir un número de razones equivalentes. Por ejemplo, al multiplicar la razón de 4.5 galones por hora por una escala de 2, se obtiene una razón de 9 galones por 2 horas. Las escalas también se usan en los mapas para indicar la relación que existe entre una distancia en el mapa y una distancia real.

U

unit rate A unit rate is a rate in which the second number (usually written as the denominator) is 1, or 1 of a quantity. For example, 1.9 children per family, 32 miles per gallon, and $\frac{3 \text{ flavors of ice cream}}{1 \text{ banana split}}$ are unit rates. Unit rates are often found by scaling other rates.

tasa unitaria Una tasa unitaria es una tasa en la que el segundo número (normalmente escrito como el denominador) es 1 ó 1 de una cantidad. Por ejemplo, 1.9 niños por familia, 32 millas por galón, y $\frac{3 \text{ sabores de helado}}{1 \text{ banana split}}$ son tasas unitarias. Las tasas unitarias se calculan a menudo aplicando escalas a otras tasas.

English/Spanish Glossary   **69**

STUDENT PAGE

Notes _____

_____

_____

_____

(69) 98

Academic Vocabulary

STUDENT PAGE

Academic vocabulary words are words that you see in textbooks and on tests. These are not math vocabulary terms, but knowing them will help you succeed in mathematics.

Las palabras de vocabulario académico son palabras que ves en los libros de texto y en las pruebas. Éstos no son términos de vocabulario de matemáticas, pero conocerlos te ayudará a tener éxito en matemáticas.

C

compare To tell or show how two things are alike and different.
related terms: analyze, relate

Sample: Compare the fraction of boys and the fraction of girls who voted for Blue.

Class Color Vote

	Blue	White	Red
Boys	19	22	16
Girls	21	16	26

A total of 57 boys and 63 girls voted. So, $\frac{19}{57}$ boys and $\frac{21}{63}$ girls voted for Blue. Both $\frac{19}{57}$ and $\frac{21}{63}$ simplify to $\frac{1}{3}$. The same fraction of boys and girls voted for Blue.

comparar Decir o mostrar en qué se parecen o en qué se diferencian dos cosas.
términos relacionados: analizar, relacionar

Ejemplo: Compara la fracción de niños y la fracción de niñas que votaron por el azul.

Voto para el Color de la clase.

	Azul	Blanco	Rojo
Niños	19	22	16
Niñas	21	16	26

En total, de 57 niños y 63 niñas votaron. Así que $\frac{19}{57}$ de los niños y $\frac{21}{63}$ de las niñas votaron por el azul. Tanto $\frac{19}{57}$ como $\frac{21}{63}$ se simplifican a $\frac{1}{3}$. La misma fracción de niños y de niñas votó por el azul.

D

describe To explain or tell in detail. A written description can contain facts and other information needed to communicate your answer. A diagram or a graph may also be included.
related terms: express, explain

Sample: A craft store sells 15 beads for $4.50 cents. Describe how to find the unit rate for the beads.

The unit rate is the price for one bead. To find the unit rate divide the total cost by the number of items. Divide 4.50 by 15. 4.50 ÷ 15 = 0.30. The unit rate for the beads is $0.30. You can also scale down the rate by dividing the rate, 15 beads for $4.50, by 5 to get 3 beads for $0.90 and then dividing by 3 to get 1 bead for $0.30.

describir Explicar o decir con detalles. Una descripción escrita puede tener datos e información necesaria para comunicar tu respuesta. También puedes incluir un diagrama o una gráfica.
términos relacionados: expresar, explicar

Ejemplo: Una tienda de artesanías vende 15 cuentas por $4.50. Describe cómo se halla la tasa unitaria de las cuentas.

La tasa unitaria es el precio de una cuenta. Para hallar la tasa unitaria, divide el costo total por el número de artículos. Divide 4.50 por 15. 4.50 ÷ 15 = 0.30. La tasa unitaria de las cuentas es $0.30.
También puedes reducir la tasa al dividir la tasa, 15 cuentas por $4.50, por 5 para obtener 3 cuentas por $0.90 y después dividir por 3 para obtener 1 cuenta por $0.30.

70 Comparing and Scaling

Notes _____

_____

_____

_____

E

explain To give facts and details that make an idea easier to understand. Explaining can involve a written summary supported by a diagram, chart, table, or a combination of these.

related terms: describe, show, justify

Sample: Valerie uses 1.5 cups of water for every cup of rice. Her rice cooker can cook a total of ten cups. What is the greatest amount of rice she can cook? Explain.

1.5 cups of water and 1 cup of rice total 2.5 cups. The ratio of rice to the total amount is 1 : 2.5. I can use a table to show she can cook 4 cups of rice.

Cups of Rice	1	2	3	4
Total Cups	2.5	5	7.5	10

I can also use a proportion.

$\frac{1}{2.5} = \frac{x}{10}$

$2.5x = 10$

$x = 4$

Valerie can cook 4 cups of rice.

explicar Dar datos y detalles que facilitan el entendimiento de una idea. Explicar puede requerir la preparación de un informe escrito apoyado por información basada en un diagrama, una tabla, un esquema o una combinación de éstos

términos relacionados: describir, mostrar, justificar

Ejemplo: Valerie usa 1.5 tazas de agua por cada taza de arroz. Su olla de arroz cocina un total de diez tazas. ¿Cuál es la mayor cantidad de arroz que puede cocinar?

1.5 tazas de agua y una taza de arroz es igual a 2.5 tazas. La razón de arroz al total es 1:2.5. Puedo usar una tabla para demostrar que debe usar 4 tazas de arroz.

Tazas de arroz	1	2	3	4
Tazas en total	2.5	5	7.5	10

También puedo usar la razón.

$\frac{1}{2.5} = \frac{x}{10}$

$2.5x = 10$

$x = 4$

Valerie puede cocinar 4 tazas de arroz.

R

relate To have a connection or impact on something else.

related terms: connect, correlate

Sample: Aman bikes 14 miles in 2 hours. Relate the time Aman bikes to the distance he travels.

The unit rate for Aman's speed is $\frac{14}{2} = 7$ miles per hour. The equation relating the distance he bikes d to time in hours h is $d = 7h$.

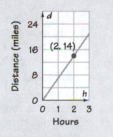

The graph and the equation both show a linear relationship between distance and time.

relacionar Haber una conexión o impacto entre una cosa y otra.

términos relacionados: unir, correlacionar

Ejemplo: Aman anda en bicicleta 14 millas en 2 horas. Relaciona el tiempo que Aman anda en bicicleta con la distancia que recorre.

La tasa unitaria de la velocidad de Aman es $\frac{14}{2} = 7$ millas por hora. La ecuación que relaciona la distancia que anda en bicicleta d con el tiempo en horas h es $d = 7h$.

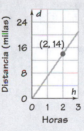

La gráfica y la ecuación demuestran una relación lineal entre distancia y tiempo.

Academic Vocabulary

Academic Vocabulary **71**

Notes _____

_____

_____

_____

Index

Notes

_____

_____

_____

_____

STUDENT PAGE

Notes _____

_____

_____

_____

Acknowledgments

Team Credits

The people who made up the **Connected Mathematics2** team—representing editorial, editorial services, design services, and production services—are listed below. Bold type denotes core team members.

Leora Adler, Judith Buice, Kerry Cashman, Patrick Culleton, Sheila DeFazio, Richard Heater, **Barbara Hollingdale, Jayne Holman,** Karen Holtzman, **Etta Jacobs,** Christine Lee, Carolyn Lock, Catherine Maglio, **Dotti Marshall,** Rich McMahon, Eve Melnechuk, Kristin Mingrone, Terri Mitchell, **Marsha Novak,** Irene Rubin, Donna Russo, Robin Samper, Siri Schwartzman, **Nancy Smith,** Emily Soltanoff, **Mark Tricca,** Paula Vergith, Roberta Warshaw, Helen Young

Additional Credits

Diana Bonfilio, Mairead Reddin, Michael Torocsik, nSight, Inc.

Illustration

Michelle Barbera: 41, 53, 67

Technical Illustration

WestWords, Inc.

Cover Design

9 Surf Studios

Photos

2 t, Richard Hutchings/PhotoEdit; **2 m,** Alden Pellett/The Image Works; **2 b,** Kevin Schafer/Corbis; **3,** M. Barrett/Robertstock.com; **5,** Stockbyte; **8,** AP Photo/Easton Star Democrat, Chris Polk; **9,** Grant Heilman Photography; **11,** PhotoDisc/Getty Images, Inc.; **16,** Russ Lappa; **18,** Ron Kimball/Ron Kimball Stock; **20,** Richard Haynes; **23,** Martin Harvey/Peter Arnold, Inc.; **25,** Richard Hutchings/PhotoEdit; **29,** Art Wolfe/Getty Images, Inc.; **30,** Ariel Skelley/Corbis; **33,** Larry Kolvoord/The Image Works; **35,** Sam Kleinman/Corbis; **36,** Digital Vision/Getty Images, Inc.; **39,** Alden Pellett/The Image Works; **41,** Peter Johansky/Index Stock Imagery; **43,** Lester Lefkowitz/Getty Images, Inc.; **46,** Kevin Radford/SuperStock; **48,** Zoran Milich/Masterfile; **52,** Renee Stockdale/Animals Animals/Earth Scenes; **55,** Felix Stensson/Alamy; **59,** Kevin Schafer/Corbis; **61,** Sandy Schaeffer/Mai/Mai/Time Life Pictures/Getty Images, Inc.; **61 frame,** Karen Beard/Getty Images, Inc.; **64,** Richard Haynes

Data Sources

The car color data on page 18 are from "Most Popular Colors by Type of Vehicle, 2001 Model Year" from THE WORLD ALMANAC. Used with permission of DuPont Automotive Products/DuPont Performance Coatings.

The radio station formats on page 18 is from "Data from U.S. Commercial Radio Stations, by Format" from THE WORLD ALMANAC. Copyright © 2002 Inside Radio.com/M Street Publications. Used by permission.

Monthly sales of *Reader's Digest* and *National Geographic* on page 21 is from FAS-FAX Report-12/31/2004. Copyright © 2004 by Audit Bureau of Circulations. All rights reserved.

The fastest bicycle speed on page 35 is from "Fastest Bicycle Speed"— Courtesy of Guinness World Records, Ltd.

The milk data on page 43 is Copyright © 2005 Holstein Association USA, Inc.

The American doctor data on page 48 are from "Doctors and Nurses: A Demographic Profile," February 1998, by Leon Bouvier. Used with permission of the Center for Immigration Studies Washington, D.C.

Note: Every effort has been made to locate the copyright owner of the material reprinted in this book. Omissions brought to our attention will be corrected in subsequent editions.

Notes _____

_____

_____

_____

Grid Paper

Labsheet 4ACE Exercise 27a

Large Grid Paper

Labsheet 4ACE Exercise 27b

Small Grid Paper

Centimeter Grid Paper

Name _____ Date _____ Class _____

Labsheet
....
for use with the Unit Project

Comparing and Scaling

Student's Guide Part (A)

Kim made up a game called *Paper Pool*. Her "tables" are rectangles traced on grid paper. There are "pockets" at each corner of the table. The pool table pockets are labeled A (bottom left corner), B (bottom right corner), C (upper right corner), and D (upper left corner). One of Kim's Paper Pool tables is shown below.

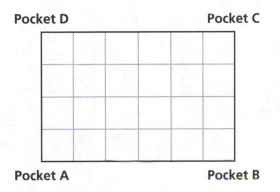

Pocket D **Pocket C**

Pocket A **Pocket B**

Kim always labels the corners in the same order shown. She describes the size of a table by giving the length of the bottom edge first and the length of the side edge second. The table shown above is a 6-by-4 Paper Pool table.

Kim's game has the following guidelines:

- The ball always starts at Pocket A.
- To move the ball, "hit" it as if you were playing pool.
- The ball always moves on a 45° diagonal across the grid.
- When the ball hits a side of the table, it bounces off at a 45° angle and continues to move.
- If the ball moves to a corner, it falls into the pocket at that corner.

Kim has played her Paper Pool game on the table below. The lines show the path that the ball traveled on the table. She notices that the ball dropped in Pocket D and that the ball has a total of 5 hits: the initial hit to get the ball moving, three hits from the ball bouncing off the sides of the table, and one hit when the ball hits the pocket and drops.

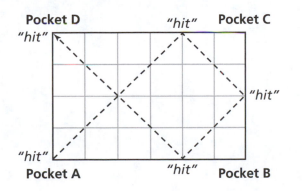

Pocket D *"hit"* **Pocket C**
"hit"

"hit"

"hit" *"hit"*
Pocket A **Pocket B**

Labsheet

Student's Guide Part (B)

Draw the path the ball would take on the two Paper Pool tables shown below. Record what pocket it drops into, how many hits occur on its journey, and the dimensions of the tables, giving the bottom length first and side length second.

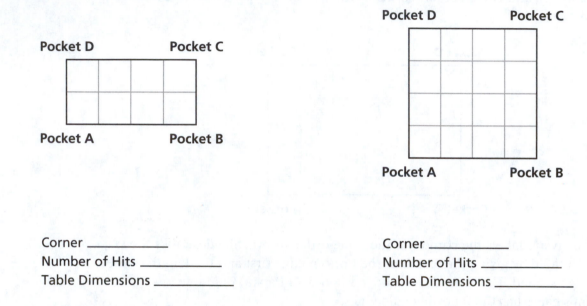

Corner _____   Corner _____
Number of Hits _____   Number of Hits _____
Table Dimensions _____   Table Dimensions _____

After playing Paper Pool on several different-sized tables, Kim wonders if there is a way to predict which pocket the ball would drop into and how many hits would occur by the time the ball drops.

Labsheet

Student's Guide Part (C)

INVESTIGATE

Explore the questions about Paper Pool that are listed below.

- Into what pocket will the ball drop?

- How many hits will occur by the time the ball drops?

Each question is asking you to notice what is happening to the ball as it travels on the Paper Pool tables. Some tables are provided (Labsheets Paper Pool A–C) to get you thinking about these questions. Make conjectures about what pocket the ball will drop into and how many hits will occur by the time the ball drops. You may need to draw additional tables on grid paper to check out any ideas you have and to test any conjectures you make.

When you think you can predict the outcomes, write a rule that you could use to determine what will happen to the ball as it travels on the Paper Pool table. This means that your rule should tell you, *without drawing the path,* the number of hits and the dropping pocket for the ball on a Paper Pool table of any size. Remember:

- The ball always starts in the bottom left corner of the table (at Pocket A).

- The ball travels on a diagonal path across the square grids.

- If the ball hits the side of the table, it bounces off at a 45° angle.

- When the ball comes to a pocket, it drops in.

REPORT

When you have finished exploring different-sized Paper Pool tables and have reached some conclusions, write a report on your work. Be sure to include the following:

1. A summary of the rules you found, why you think your rules are correct, and anything else you discovered. (You might discuss what you noticed as you examined the paths for the different tables and what helped you to arrive at your rules.)

2. For each rule given, draw one new Paper Pool table (not from the ones given to you) that shows that your rule accurately predicts what happens.

3. Include your drawings of ball paths on the given Paper Pool tables as well as any additional Paper Pool tables you made to help you write your rules.

4. Include any tables, charts, or other tools you used to help you organize your information and look for patterns that would lead to rules.

5. Explain any other patterns or ideas about Paper Pool tables and the path of the ball that you observed. (For example, on which tables does the ball's path follow the same basic course? For which tables does the design traced by the ball's path look the same?)

Labsheet

Student's Guide Part (D)

EXTENSION QUESTION

Can you predict the length of the path the ball will travel on any size Paper Pool table? Suppose each time the ball crosses a square, the distance it travels is "one diagonal unit." How many diagonal units is the path of the ball?

One Diagonal
Unit

Length of Path:
6 Diagonal Units

Labsheet

Paper Pool A

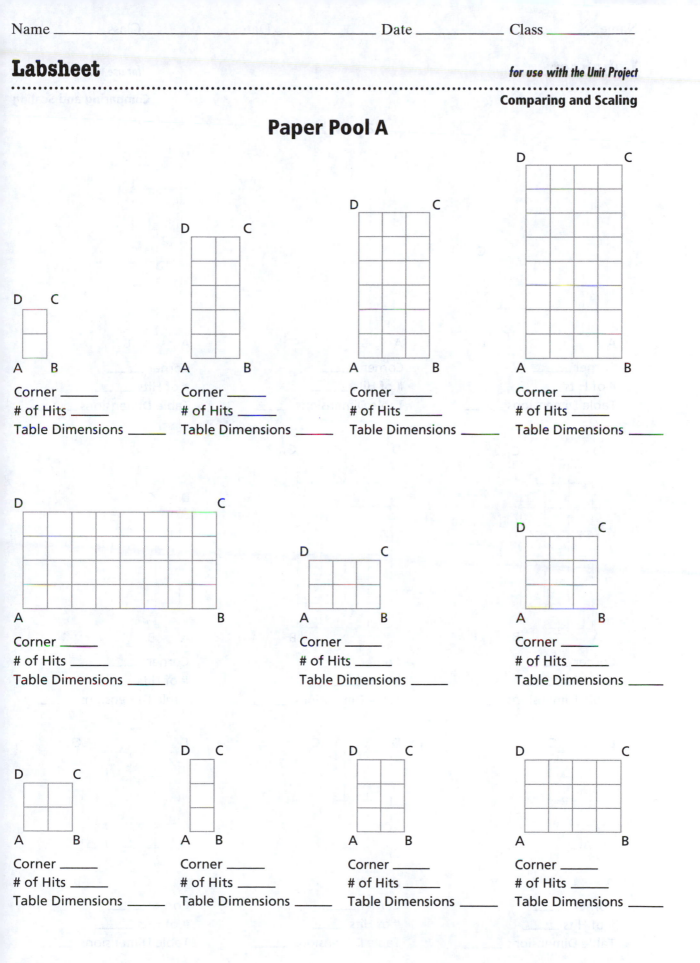

Corner _____
# of Hits _____
Table Dimensions _____

Corner _____
# of Hits _____
Table Dimensions _____

Corner _____
# of Hits _____
Table Dimensions _____

Corner _____
# of Hits _____
Table Dimensions _____

Corner _____
# of Hits _____
Table Dimensions _____

Corner _____
# of Hits _____
Table Dimensions _____

Corner _____
# of Hits _____
Table Dimensions _____

Corner _____
# of Hits _____
Table Dimensions _____

Corner _____
# of Hits _____
Table Dimensions _____

Corner _____
# of Hits _____
Table Dimensions _____

Corner _____
# of Hits _____
Table Dimensions _____

Labsheet

Paper Pool B

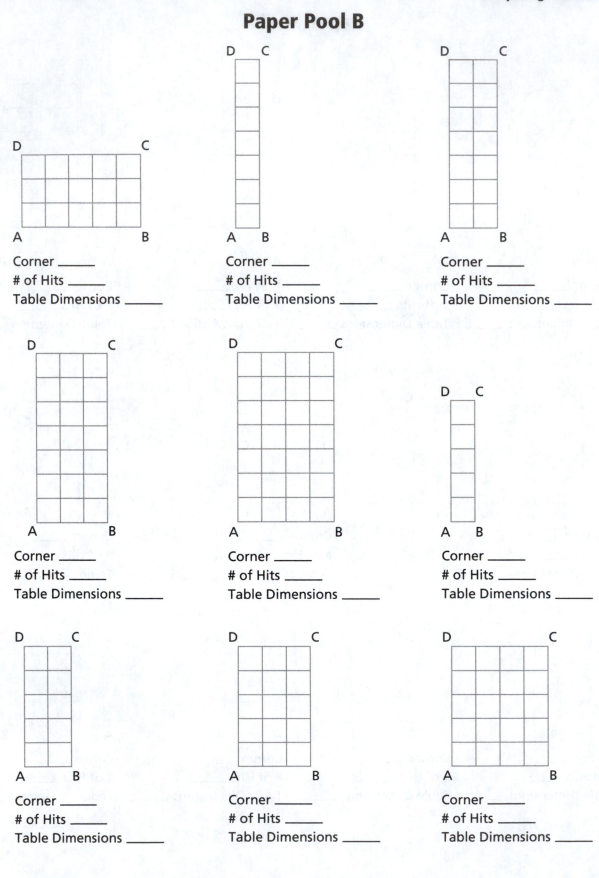

Corner _____
# of Hits _____
Table Dimensions _____

Corner _____
# of Hits _____
Table Dimensions _____

Corner _____
# of Hits _____
Table Dimensions _____

Corner _____
# of Hits _____
Table Dimensions _____

Corner _____
# of Hits _____
Table Dimensions _____

Corner _____
# of Hits _____
Table Dimensions _____

Corner _____
# of Hits _____
Table Dimensions _____

Corner _____
# of Hits _____
Table Dimensions _____

Corner _____
# of Hits _____
Table Dimensions _____

Labsheet

Paper Pool C

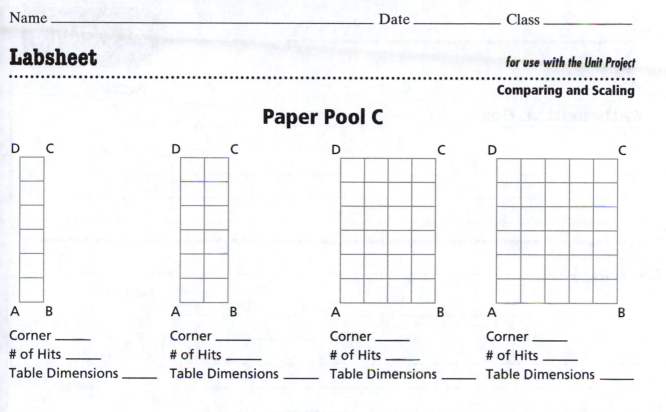

Corner _____
# of Hits _____
Table Dimensions _____

Corner _____
# of Hits _____
Table Dimensions _____

Corner _____
# of Hits _____
Table Dimensions _____

Corner _____
# of Hits _____
Table Dimensions _____

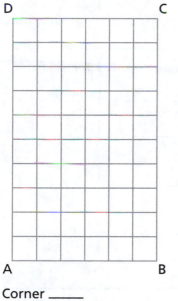

Corner _____
# of Hits _____
Table Dimensions _____

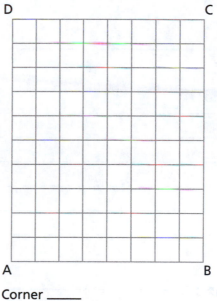

Corner _____
# of Hits _____
Table Dimensions _____

Mathematical Goals

Launch

Materials

Explore

Materials

Summarize

Materials

Glossary

P

proportion An equation stating that two ratios are equal. For example:

$$\frac{\text{hours spent on homework}}{\text{hours spent in school}} = \frac{2}{7}$$

Note that this does not necessarily imply that "hours spent on homework" = 2 or that "hours spent in school" = 7. During a week, 10 hours may have been spent on homework while 35 hours were spent in school. The proportion is still true because $\frac{10}{35} = \frac{2}{7}$.

R

rate A comparison of quantities measured in two different units is called a rate. A rate can be thought of as a direct comparison of two sets (20 cookies for 5 children) or as an average amount (4 cookies per child). A rate such as 5.5 miles per hour can be written as $\frac{5.5 \text{ miles}}{1 \text{ hour}}$, or 5.5 miles : 1 hour.

rate table You can use a rate to find and organize equivalent rates in a rate table. For example, you can use the rate "five limes for $1.00" to make this rate table.

Cost of Limes

Number of Limes	Cost of Limes
1	$0.20
2	$0.40
3	$0.60
4	$0.80
5	$1.00
10	$2.00
15	$3.00
20	$4.00

ratio A ratio is a number, often expressed as a fraction, used to make comparisons between two quantities. Ratios may also be expressed as equivalent decimals or percents, or given in the form $a : b$. Here are some examples of uses of ratios:

- The ratio of females to males on the swim team is 2 to 3, or $\frac{2 \text{ females}}{3 \text{ males}}$.
- The train travels at a speed of 80 miles per hour, or $\frac{80 \text{ miles}}{1 \text{ hour}}$.
- If a small figure is enlarged by a scale factor of 2, the new figure will have an area four times its original size. The ratio of the small figure's area to the large figure's area will be $\frac{1}{4}$. The ratio of the large figure's area to the small figure's area will be $\frac{4}{1}$, or 4.
- In the example above, the ratio of the length of a side of the small figure to the length of the corresponding side of the large figure is $\frac{1}{2}$. The ratio of the length of a side in the large figure to the length of the corresponding side in the small figure is $\frac{2}{1}$, or 2.

S

scale, scaling The scale is the number used to multiply both parts of a ratio to produce an equal, but possibly more informative, ratio. A ratio can be scaled to produce a number of equivalent ratios. For example, multiplying the rate of 4.5 gallons per hour by a scale of 2 yields the rate of 9 gallons per 2 hours. Scales are also used on maps to give the relationship between a measurement on the map to the actual physical measurement.

U

unit rate A unit rate is a rate in which the second number (usually written as the denominator) is 1, or 1 of a quantity. For example, 1.9 children per family, 32 miles per gallon, and $\frac{3 \text{ flavors of ice cream}}{1 \text{ banana split}}$ are unit rates. Unit rates are often found by scaling other rates.

Index

Acknowledgments

Team Credits

The people who made up the **Connected Mathematics2** team—representing editorial, editorial services, design services, and production services—are listed below. Bold type denotes core team members.

Leora Adler, Judith Buice, Kerry Cashman, Patrick Culleton, Sheila DeFazio, Richard Heater, **Barbara Hollingdale, Jayne Holman,** Karen Holtzman, **Etta Jacobs,** Christine Lee, Carolyn Lock, Catherine Maglio, **Dotti Marshall,** Rich McMahon, Eve Melnechuk, Kristin Mingrone, Terri Mitchell, **Marsha Novak,** Irene Rubin, Donna Russo, Robin Samper, Siri Schwartzman, **Nancy Smith,** Emily Soltanoff, **Mark Tricca,** Paula Vergith, Roberta Warshaw, Helen Young

Additional Credits

Diana Bonfilio, Mairead Reddin, Michael Torocsik, nSight, Inc.

Technical Illustration

Schawk, Inc.

Cover Design

tom white.images

JEROME LIBRARY
CURRICULUM RESOURCE CENTER
BOWLING GREEN STATE UNIVERSITY
BOWLING GREEN, OHIO 43403

DATE DUE

OCT 19 2008		
OCT 29 REC'D		
NOV 19 2009		
DEC 22 REC'D		
OhioLINK		
JAN 2 6 2017		
GAYLORD		PRINTED IN U.S.A.

CURR 510 P92c2 /2 gr.7 v.3

Connected mathematics 2.

BOWLING GREEN, OHIO 43403